The Story of a Boy, His Father, a Paper Route and
12 Secrets of Serving Others in Business and Life

by
Steven J. Anderson

Illustrations by
Peter Arkle

Published in 2022
by The Yes Press

Library of Congress Control Number: 2021917308
Library of Congress Cataloging-in-Publication Data
1. Anderson, Steven J. 2. Management. I. Title

ISBN 978-0-578-97470-5
Printed in the United States of America
The Yes Press • Dallas, Texas
1st Printing, 2022

The Bicycle Book / Steven J. Anderson

Illustrations by Peter Arkle
Cover design by Jesse Brand
Book designed by Ed Brinton
Book edited by Mike Steere

Dedicated to my father,
Arthur S. Anderson

Whosoever shall do and teach...
the same shall be called great.

– Matthew 5:19

Contents

Foreword

Enjoy the Ride

This book belongs to a genre that I call the autobiographical business novel. It's partly a tale of my boyhood paper route, partly a how-to guide to understanding and taking action to better serve people in business and life. Some of the more made-up-seeming parts are, in fact, factual. For example, a customer I never met before did appear and ceremoniously present to me the exact book I needed to read at that moment. Strange and kinda magic, especially to a twelve-year-old. But it was real, and that book remains a powerful influence.

Some happenings, on the other hand, are reconstructed. Still, they're based on things that occurred, true to situations and true to character. It's absolutely true that my advertising executive Dad was a wonderfully gifted teacher who favored Socratic dialogue over one-way fatherly lecturing. And, at dinner, he conducted a sort of running Q&A seminar and coaching on challenges I met serving my paper route customers. There, at the dinner table, he laid out the lessons about customer service that this book is meant to teach.

Are the conversations as written accurate? Of course not. I wasn't wired, and there are no transcripts. But the lessons my father imparts are rock-solid-true to what he taught me and true to the way he taught in word and in deed.

Why Go Back to 1978?

With specific, actionable information to impart, I decided to teach the way I was taught—through experiences with people on my paper route followed by dialoguing with Dad. Each chapter winds up with a "Get Pedaling" section full of practical applications for you. Real-time. Real business. Real life.

The decision to go this route, starting with teachable moments in my boyhood and Dad's mentoring, was calculated. If I had seen another, better way to go, I surely would have. But stories seemed to work. So I started to work them.

And, right from the get-go, they worked me.

What started out as compact case studies came alive more completely than I ever expected, in my mind and then on the page. This thing became a full-on story that demanded to be told in its own way.

The Bicycle Book was a ride I went along on. I had no choice. After I relaxed and found my balance—as I once learned to balance my Schwinn Sting-Ray bike loaded down with newspapers—I didn't want a choice. I love the ride, which goes on and on. With the door to the past kicked open, I find new surprises in it, learn new lessons from things that happened and things that were said more than forty years ago.

I hope you have an opportunity similar to the one I just had. I hope you take some time to tell yourself the story of an important part of your life. It's a great adventure that should not be missed, with lessons for life that never stop coming.

Meanwhile, I sincerely hope you take the time to get the most out of my boyhood adventures in customer relations, to absorb their meaning and get takeaways for your business and life right now.

Go slowly. Be there with me back then. Be with my people; sit down with us at the table. Get to each chapter's lessons and to-dos for the present the way I did, by living challenges and benefitting from my father's business wisdom and generous understanding of other people. You'll find your own powerful lessons for a lifetime. You'll remember the story and, like me, you'll keep learning after you put the book down. The story does keep teaching. With re-reading, you'll discover more lessons between the lines.

Besides the teaching, there's enjoyment to be had. There's respite from our time of bitterness and division. The past reminds us to be nicer to each other, as we once were and still can be.

Then, having gone slowly, speed up and take action with the practical how-tos that end each chapter.

Accidental Parenting Handbook

Just as I didn't mean to do a memoir/business hybrid, I didn't mean to create a handbook on parenting; I didn't realize I had until I was nearly done. But Dad demonstrates how to be a powerful, positive influence on his kids. In practice and principle he's old-school, but he never falls back on parental prerogative and bigfoots his children as parents, especially fathers, can do. He's attentive to the needs, in the moment, of each individual child. And he walks the parental talk. Example is an extremely powerful teacher. So is making yourself an open book and doing your best to help kids benefit from your experience and apply it to their own.

Fathers and mothers, teachers, coaches, and mentors can learn a lot from spending time with Dad.

Lessons of the Schwinn Sting-Ray

We can learn a lot, too, from the late Al Fritz, father of the Schwinn Sting-Ray bicycle. A purple Sting-Ray is the steed I rode on my paper route, still supercool to me in 1978 even though it was a hand-me-down from an older brother and the design was already fifteen years old.

Fritz, a Schwinn executive, did not originate the idea of making kid-size bikes tricked out with tall ape-hanger handlebars, long banana seats, and wild colors. Kids in California did it first on their own, customizing their bikes so they looked like chopper motorcycles and hot rods. Fritz went out to California to take a look and decided to factory-build the same sort of bikes. Other company execs jeered, but the things sold out. In a few years, 60 percent of new American bikes were Sting-Rays and knockoffs.

All the guy did was pay close attention to kids, much as Dad did. Or, in the broader customer-service context of this book, he let an important clientele show him how they wanted to be served, and he served them accordingly. And he sold millions of bikes.

Nobody in my family has any idea where our original purple Sting-Ray went. Some years back I shelled out $500 for an authentic vintage 1965 replacement. These days I'd pay a lot more for what was—and for some people still is—the coolest bike in the known universe.

Enjoy the ride.

Prologue

Salt Lake City, Utah
January, 1978
Dinnertime Midweek

Purpose Is Us

This table once fit Mom, Dad, and all of their four boys and three girls. Then, with seventeen years between the firstborn and the youngest (me), kids grew up and left. Now we're down to two sisters and me, and five feels skimpy for so much table. But the table's shape—round—still serves a special purpose beyond gathering to savor Mom's amazing home cooking.

Purpose is us, the Andersons.

Very, very little happens by accident in our 1950s brick house on Kensington Avenue. We eat at an expandable round table with the same functional benefits King Arthur enjoyed with his Knights of the Round Table. Roundness—no sharp corners between people—works for inclusive and free verbal exchange.

Our talky family dinners, like pretty much everything, are a coordinated two-parent effort. Mom runs food prep, table-setting, and serving on a precise schedule. Disorder is terrified of Janice Virginia Jacobsen Anderson. It has bad dreams about her and wakes up yelling. I can still recall the timing of daily routines and tell you where I sit at dinner. As the last born, I've been next to Mom since I spit back strained peas in my highchair. Dad's at Mom's other side, inseparable in body and spirit. Beautiful to see them then and beautiful to remember now. Also highly functional and, yes, purposeful.

If you don't see past the fantastic cooking and homemaking, you miss the Real Mom. I can't even imagine the disarray without her oversight and management. Picture dazed, lost-looking Andersons yelling, "Mom" "Jan!" while the house collapses in a pile of bricks and un-balanced checkbooks, past-due bills, unsigned school forms, overlooked and undone whatever.

Yes, I exaggerate. But not by a lot. For all of Dad's vision, we rely on Mom's genius for management and detail. She excels as our Chief Operations Officer and Chief Financial Officer, which completes the family C-Suite.

We sit down to dinner at 6:30. Dad will charge out of his office at the big advertising agency he heads and come flying through the door exactly on time. When conversation commences, he presides over table talk meant to do one or more of us some good. But there's no "Because I'm your Father!" or talking-down-to, and nobody minds speaking up. Dad leads us to wisdom with his own amiable home version of the ancient Greek philosopher Socrates'

Q&A Dialogues. He asks us questions, listens, makes us think. If he weren't so good at it, I would not have a book's worth of valuable lessons from my growing-up years in Salt Lake.

It Is Time, My Son

Amen!

After the prayer ends, there's some quiet digging in that takes the edge off my gnawing kid hunger. Dad leans forward to look around Mom at me.

"Well, are you ready?"

The way he smiles, it's a good thing I'm supposed to be ready for. But what?

"How old are you now?"

Again, what? He knows my age perfectly well.

"Refresh my memory, Steven. Whose birthday did we celebrate last week?"

"Um, mine?" I look deeply into my mashed potatoes, which will not notice I am baffled.

"And how many candles were on the cake?"

"Twelve."

"Right you are! And what happens when a young man in this house turns twelve?"

Dad proclaims his own answer: "My son, it is time for you to start delivering newspapers!"

In truth, I already know but am not thinking of it. No way in the world could I not know I will have a paper route. My three older brothers delivered the afternoon daily *Deseret News* in succession, each handing on the same route in our neighborhood to the next-youngest. Then, due to lack of paper-route-age boys, came a long gap that just ended. Now I will assume the mantle, honor tradition, but there's way more to it than that.

Delivering papers reliably and on time, to subscribers' satisfaction and sky-high standards of service inspired by Dad, is not an option. It is a condition of growing up a male Anderson, an obligatory rite of passage. In other age-counting systems, people say kids after their twelfth birthdays are thirteen because they're in their thirteenth year. The age has great significance in many cultures. In my family culture, becoming a paperboy really means becoming a paper young man.

It's also one of My Parents' Top Three Non-Negotiables:

1. Everybody takes piano lessons and practices daily, like it or not. I've been doing it since age eight.
2. At age twelve, boys get a paper route.
3. This one's also gender-specific, tied to turning twelve, and will kick in for me very soon. Details to come in the chapter after next.

I call these things Non-Negotiables now, not then. Back in the day they're just part of a well-ordered life that even I as a kid appreciate as pretty darn good. I've always known they were coming.

But maybe not so abruptly at dinner.

Dad beams like I just won Big Lotto. "You are in luck!" he says. "I called Mrs. Hanson, the route supervisor, today. Your brothers' old route just opened up, and you can start next week!"

"Great!"

I don't 100 percent mean it. This is a lot to process. It is great that I'm old enough to take on work that gets me out of the house, doing more than kid chores, for more money. An actual job! But I know what the job entails. A big piece of my afternoons will now belong to the *Deseret News* home delivery system and a bunch of subscribers that I know from family paper route lore can be a pain. Riding around and firing papers at porches with cool-kid style appeals, for sure, but that's only part of the job. The notion of a job itself resonates way down deep where I feel rather than think—and it's kinda scary. Take a step out of childhood and you can't step back. You can't un-grow, especially not in this house. Work, responsibility, accountability start now and will not stop until I am older than Dad and can't work any more.

No going back.

I need another moment with the potatoes.

Purple With Purpose

No, what I really need is a moment with my purple Schwinn Sting-Ray.

It leans against a wall in the garage and wears its years and miles with pride. It's as old as I am, not a hand-me-down but an honored legacy. My older brother had it. When I was tiny I would watch him doing crazy big-boy stuff on it, dyin' to pop wheelies myself, whoop airborne off curbs, and, yes, hang bags stuffed with folded newspapers on the ape-hanger bars and ride my own paper route. A kid on-purpose doing a job was even bigger in my eyes than a pedaling hot-rodder. Since I grew into the bike, I am already that. Now that I have real business in the real world, this will be my commercial delivery vehicle. It has, of course, served the same purpose before. I like the idea that one of us has some experience.

That unease back at dinner, when Dad told me out of the blue about the paper route, came and went. Looking long at my grape-colored vehicle I am ready, man, thrilled—and glad to be that way in private. Bike, you and I have new places to go.

"Steve?"

Trust a big sister to mess up my moment. It's Heidi, four years older, self-tasked with riding herd on Little Brother.

"Why'd you sneak up on me?"

"I didn't. You were just standing there, staring at the bike. I think you were talking to it."

"What do you want, Heidi?"

"I don't want anything. Dad does. He told me to come find you."

FIRST
NATIONAL
BANK
Where People
Mean Everything

Chapter 1

Where People Mean Everything

Step One

I am in deeper than I think, starting this paper route. Dad gets it and gets that I probably don't, which is why he summons me through my supervisory big sister so we can (a) figure it out and (b) deal with it. Looking back, I say hats off to the genius newspaper company who made home delivery a can't-lose proposition for itself. At age twelve I am an independent contractor with attendant responsibilities, obligations, and even some downside risk. After the bundled papers are dropped off on the driveway every afternoon, the whole deal is on the paperboy. Me.

Dad begins: "You need to understand that you are responsible for more than delivery. You also collect money from each and every customer on your route on a monthly basis. Where do you think you should keep that money until you have to pay the company for the papers you deliver?"

"A bank, I guess?"

"That's easy, then. You can use your current checking account." Dad can't pass up a chance for a little joke.

He goes on to tell me we already have an appointment for after school tomorrow to open an account at First National Bank.

"I moved a couple things around on my schedule to be there. Do not be late!"

"I'll be there."

"Okay, I'll meet you at First National. What time did we say?"

I tell him.

"Oh, another thing…"

"Yes?"

"Have you practiced your piano?"

Paper route Step One. Run and done.

High Finance

Done and ride, actually. From my front yard in Salt Lake, I look up at mountains laden with the world's best deep powder snow for skiing and boarding. Snow comes and goes down here during the winter, and our bank day happens to be bike-able.

Bare pavement does not mean it's warm out, but so what? The wind freezes my face because I'm booking it. To a financial institution. To become a client. For, wait for it, professional purposes! Is this amazing or what?

Could it be more obvious that I was born to go into business? Nurture alone would not explain such wild excitement about a trip to a bank. Nature has to be in on it, too—in the genes and brain wiring.

If you're early, you are on time. I am both.

I park the Sting-Ray by the marbled, brassy bank entrance under the sign that reads:

First National Bank

Where People Mean Everything

The words connect to what I see next: A deep blue Chrysler New Yorker pulls up. From it steps a man wearing two out of three pieces of a perfectly pressed suit; the fabric is an even classier blue than the car. The starched shirt blazes white against the vest while he opens the back car door to get the suit jacket, which he puts on with care.

Boy, can Dad wear a suit. Giving credit where it's due, boy can Mac Christiansen, legendary Utah clothier, hang suits on select clients. Unlike other VIPs in his age cohort, Dad doesn't need master tailoring to camouflage middle-age spread. He stands straight and trim and about as fit as a man of 55 years can be. His long, bespectacled face stretches down to a lantern jaw and radiates good humor. It's a face good for being funny, a lot like the now-vintage funnyman Dick Van Dyke, except Dad never clowns or works for laughs. The world entertains him, rather than vice versa, and you can't help but get caught up.

He lights up as he sees me and strides with confidence—more than a walk, the way the Mr. Mac masterpiece is more than a suit—toward me. "Hello, Mr. Anderson. My apologies for being almost late," he says and puts his hand out for a manly shake. The hand then goes to my shoulder, and we stop together and look up at the sign on the bank: Where People Mean Everything.

"We will need to have a talk about the words up there," Dad says, "but come on, people are waiting."

Big Dealness

I have known for as long as I can remember where the words come from. My dad, who heads the Intermountain West's largest advertising agency, dreamed them up and landed the bank as a client. The four words tell the story the bank wants told so perfectly that it has used them as its slogan for years and years and will continue to do so into my young manhood. We in the family know the slogan as a Dad all-time hit. In my admiring eyes, it adds to my father's already big big-dealness.

But look at this. I am a big deal, too.

A very bank-y woman with a great smile greets us.

"Mr. Anderson—or should I say Misters Anderson?—it is so good to see you! Thank you for coming in." Then, turning to me, "You must be Steven. I'm Jane, the New Accounts Manager, and I will be helping you today."

Parental politeness training kicks in so I shake the extended hand, a very nice one, and meet her gaze. "Very pleased to meet you."

"Please call me Jane."

First-naming a grownup is new, but if it's what she wants, fine. Obviously, this is a high point of Jane's day, meeting the top new customer.

I am now a few inches taller.

Jane walks us, me first and Dad right behind, into her office. She hesitates about which way to slide the paperwork on her desk, all ready to be filled out and signed. Dad says to me, "Your account, not mine. I'm here to just co-sign."

While I fill out the forms with great care in A-plus penmanship, Dad tells Jane about the ins and outs of the paper route with emphasis on bookkeeping and cash flow, some of which is news to me.

"Wow, that is a lot of responsibility!" After Dad and I have signed, Jane gives me temporary checks, deposit slips, and official new account what-all and says, "We are so glad to have you as a new customer. Let us know how we can meet all your banking needs. My phone extension is here on my card, Mr. Anderson."

"Thank you. And please, call me Steve."

Jane is wowed by me and my new business. I am impressed with her and the whole bank living up to Dad's slogan.

It feels amazingly great to be a People Who Mean Everything in this place full of money.

Love it, love it, love it. I could really get used to this.

Takeaway

Back out front, we gaze up once again at Where People Mean Everything. The day seems less chilly.

"You know," says Dad, "It is amazing what happens when a business makes a promise as to how it will serve its clientele and repeats that promise to the world. People on the inside rise to the promise. If the words are truly meant, other people want to do business and keep doing it."

He thinks for a few seconds.

"A bank's job is to very carefully handle and protect people's money, like yours."

"I understand."

"So if that's their job, why isn't it, 'Where Money Means Everything' or 'People's Money' or 'Your Money?'"

"I'm not sure."

"Think about it. Did Jane say, 'We're glad to have your money here?' or, 'We are glad to grab you so young so you'll stick with us when you grow up and maybe make buckets of money?'"

"Uh, no."

"She did not. She said, in so many words, 'We're glad to have *you*, and you are *everything* for us.' And how did that make you feel?"

"I really liked it."

"Do you want to keep coming back and feeling this way?"

"Of course."

"There's a lesson here. It applies to everybody in every business. In everything, really. Put people up front, keep them there, and they'll make you and your business very successful. First and foremost come the people. Do you think this will work for you on your paper route?"

"So it's not about the papers?"

"It's not about the newspapers so much as how reliable and responsible you are, how you earn and go on earning people's trust. That sets you apart. You live up to a personal promise. So, what do you think yours will be?"

"What do you mean?"

"Your promise. In your words. If you can't say what it is, how can you live up to it? What is your promise going to be?"

Instant brain block. Nothing comes to mind, except…

"In the agency, we just start throwing out ideas."

Except…

"I want to use that one, Dad. Yours."

He ahems and says, "You know, the bank pays us good money for that slogan. It's worth a lot."

Okay, there goes that.

"But maybe, just maybe, I will let you borrow it. But you can't tell anybody."

Dad proposes an arrangement that nobody else in the world can ever know about. Under the table, off the books, very hush-hush.

"The slogan is yours, Steven. Your own four-word promise to customers and yourself. Never forget this is something you are committed to. Anything less breaks the promise. What happens then?"

"I lose all my customers and go broke."

"There is that, yes," Dad says. "You disappoint the people. Letting other people down is one thing. What about letting yourself down?"

He looks at his watch. "I've got to get to a meeting. See you at dinner."

He strides, not walks, to the Chrysler. I put up the kickstand and straddle the cold seat.

This is my 4,754th day on Earth, and it's one of the great ones.

Get Pedaling

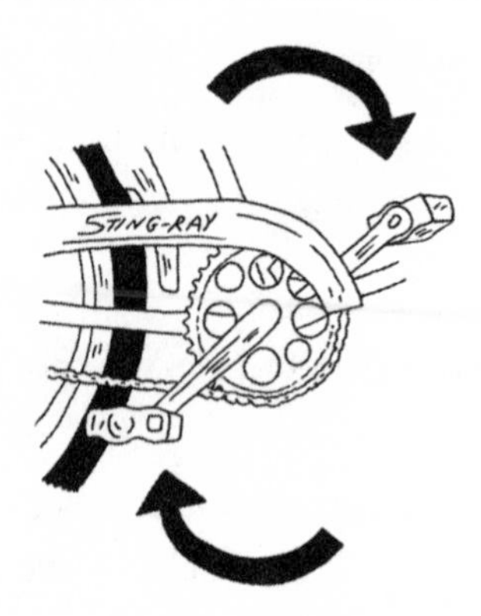

The Challenge

Find the words to express your unique promise to the people you serve. This is also a promise to yourself and your team about how you will serve in spirit and process.

The promise, squeezed down into a phrase or short sentence, is simple, easy to remember and to act on every day.

More Than a Catchphrase

There is immense power in promises made and kept. Memorable examples have changed business history.

Consider the rental car company Avis' all-time classic "We Try Harder." It dates to 1963, when Avis was a distant second to Hertz and bleeding money. In one year the company became profitable and began to gain market share. For fifty years, the three words worked brilliantly to inspire Avis team members to deliver exceptional service.

"Ladies and gentlemen serving ladies and gentlemen." The exclusive Ritz-Carlton hotel chain continues to use this as an in-house credo for its team members. It's legendary for defining a winning service culture.

Such service promises speak both to present and future clients and those serving them. They say, basically, "This is who we are and our pledge to you."

Think about the two-way messaging in other classic promises:

> "Have it your way."
> – Burger King

> "The relentless pursuit of perfection."
> – Lexus Automobiles

> "You're in good hands."
> – Allstate Insurance (in use since the 1950s)

Forbidden Words

Avoid such words as Leading, Best, Quality, Most Reliable, Oldest. They are really bragging about you, not the people you serve and what you promise to do for them.

People, Not Things

Whatever the specifics of your service—custom kitchens, adult orthodontics, unclogging drains—the essence is human, one person to another, not the tangible and/or technical.

Here are a few examples from fields where service depends on special technical expertise:

> "We care for the person attached to teeth."
> (Family dentistry)
>
> "We look beyond the eyes."
> (Optometry)
>
> "The Punctual Plumber."
> (Home repair and installation)

Word Choice

If you struggle with a whole phrase, start by playing with key concepts and words that get to the point. Then roll each word around and think deep about its meaning.

In the First National Bank tagline—its promise—the first word is "Where." Why? Well, in those pre-virtual days a bank was an actual place. Even with only three more words, and the same message in mind, there were lots of choices about wordage. It could have been "Where You Mean Everything" instead of "Where People . . ." but people is both warm and more encompassing, good things for a bank to be. "People Mean…" is more powerful than

"People Are..." because meaning is really a choice to be made and acted on in this special place. "Everything" is what people want to mean to others focused on their needs.

You get the idea. Make your promise in words that say it all, succinctly and with power.

In Mind and Out Loud

Make a plan to keep the promise front and center in your own mind. Print it up on a wallet-sized note card. Use it as a daily mantra with your entire team. Make it part of in-house messaging. Discuss it. Post it. Come back to it in team meetings. Recognize, on a regular basis, efforts to live up to the promise.

You may or may not decide to make your service promise part of your marketing message. Either way, your job is to define it, operationalize it, and make it part of how you do business every day.

So...

What's your service promise?

NEWS
Schwinn
STING-RAY

Chapter 2

What Everything Means to People

Starting With a Bang

The BANG being the Sting-Ray crashing down sideways against the garage floor, with added impetus from two brand-new canvas route bags packed with folded papers. Some of the papers get loose and skitter away like they're scared. They ought to be on Paper Route Day One.

On the upside, doing things wrong can eventually get you to right. I now know one more way not to load up. I already know that full, tight-packed bags are too heavy for me to lift and hang on the grips of the Sting-Ray's tall handlebars. I attempt—and fail—to solve the problem by hanging the bags and then finishing loading.

Before that came folding the papers with advertising stuffers and rubber-banding them. That couldn't happen until after the truck stopped at the end of the driveway and guys dropped bundled papers and ad stuffers, the new canvas bags, a list of newly added and dropped customers from the list I already have, and at least one billion rubber bands. Thankfully, Day One's truck came early in the time window for drop-offs, giving me more time to lug everything into the garage and get going. If it had come any later, I would be even more behind.

All this gets me to the aforementioned BANG and one last *aha!* moment: The fully loaded bike won't balance unless I straddle it. Since I can't un-straddle, I gotta roll.

Pushin' pedals and pitchin' papers, baby—here I go!

Better and Better

With a full load of papers hanging from the tall bars, this is not the Sting-Ray I know. But I gut it out and survive the wobbly turn at the end of the driveway.

I'm really glad nobody's home at my first house. I ride right up to the steps so as not to attempt the full paperboy pitch from sidewalk to the porch. Then—this is embarrassing even without witnesses—I kick the bike backwards down the front walk.

At the eighth or ninth house, the most wonderful thing happens. A grandmotherly lady stands out on the walk.

"You must be Steve," she says. "We've been expecting you."

"It's so good to meet you, Mrs. Fergus."

Yes, I've been checking the subscriber list as I go.

"Mr. Fergus is inside waiting to get all worked up and yell about the news."

What a sweet human being is this, first of the People Who Mean Everything it is my great pleasure to serve.

"We'll chat some other time," says Mrs. Fergus. "I know you have many more valued customers waiting."

Score! I personally connect with a customer. And I am pleased that this special Where People Mean Everything thing I dreamed up works. By prior arrangement, my predecessor delivered his last papers with a friendly Hello note from me, my home phone number included. Dad Q&A'd me about whether paying to Xerox the note and compensate the other guy was a worthwhile investment. He undoubtedly knew then what I know now: Without the note, Mrs.

Fergus would not know upfront that I'm Steve who cares so much he writes notes and gives all customers his personal number.

Another really nice lady hears me coming up the walk and walks out looking, I think, concerned for me. She loves it when I personally hand her the paper.

An old-ish guy comes out, grumpy but still encouraging, saying he expects I'll get the hang of it and deliver his paper at the same time as the other kid. Customers who meet and greet are a minority. If they were all like Mrs. Simpson, I'd take forever to finish. Mrs. Simpson cannot doubt she means everything while I hear about her son's promotion and transfer, and missing her grandchildren, who really are cute in pictures. And so smart in school.

Personal encounters slack off at dinner hour. Having met such super-friendly customers, I'm pretty sure I can count on understanding from those who get their papers after the company's promised six o'clock delivery. The latest should be only be about 40–45 minutes overdue. Not bad for a first timer who more than makes up for it by nailing Where People Mean Everything.

Where do they mean everything? Right here, on Steve's friendly paper route, that's where.

Bombs Fall at Dinner

I run in after dinner starts and still get a triumphal welcome. Even my sisters are all smiles.

"All hail the man who is gainfully employed!" booms Dad.

"Go wash your hands; your dinner's getting cold," Mom says.

I tell how great it went, emphasis on living up to the slogan and warm-fuzzies with customers who came out to see me in person. My arrival time back home tells the story of lateness, but that's more like a footnote.

Dad seems to concur. He goes into thinking-out-loud mode. "So, you put people first, and they put you first, is that how it goes? And the meet-and-greets are time well spent…"

Serious job-well-done props coming up next, I know it.

Dad asks, "Well, did you meet Mr. Newell? Over on Logan Avenue?"

"I could have. I'll have to check my list."

Dad rattles off a couple more names and avenues, and I ask him how he knows these people on my route.

"Can't say that I do know them, except over the phone. They did seem quite nice, considering they were all waiting for their papers, and maybe still are."

Oh no.

Mom chimes in that Mr. McPhee got his paper, but without the ad stuffer. He's upset because today's the day he and Mrs. McPhee clip coupons and go over the specials at Smith's Food King. They like going through all the other ads, too.

"People buy papers for the advertising as much as the editorial content," Dad observes.

Now Mom drops a bomb. Her friend Clara Baldwin called before Dad got home, saying she just saw me ride past her house without delivering the paper. Bud Baldwin would have a conniption if he didn't get his paper.

"I took ours and walked it over," Mom says. Dad lifts his eyebrows at me to signal that Mom went way out of her way to save my you-know-what.

"Thank you, Mom."

"Well, you know, that was a favor to a special friend. Clara and I went to school together. And everybody knows how Bud can be."

The other two at the table go to Big Sister Heaven, seeing their kid brother whiplashed from way-too-happy-and-proud to failure and carpet-bombing by both parents.

Dad drops a bunker buster: "Just before dinner your route supervisor, Mrs. Hanson, called. Your Mom and I both got on the line."

"Am I fired?" No matter what the answer, even if I can't be an Anderson anymore because I got terminated from a Parental Non-Negotiable, I refuse to cry at the dinner table.

But Dad leans toward me with love all over his face, and smiles. "Relax, Son. First days can be worst days. Mrs. Hanson wanted us, especially you, not to worry about any missed deliveries. There's a radio-dispatched driver that takes care of them. She said to tell you there have been worse first days than yours. You do, however, want to get up to speed."

"I will! I promise to work harder."

"Hard may be less of an issue than what you work at."

He looks up and summons the spirit of Socrates.

Right, Right, Right

"What can you tell me about the three R's, Steve?"

"Reading, writing?"

"You're in business, not second grade. I'll give you a clue—Right, Right, Right."

"Right attitude, right work habits, right, ummm..." I'm just guessing. Please, Dad, this has been a long day.

Dad shortcuts the Q&A to get us to what Right, Right, Right means and do a quick review:

"Again, what it is they want, that they're paying you for, which is the same as anybody providing a tangible deliverable—a toaster, a car, a newspaper?"

"Right Product."

"And?"

"Right Place."

"And you forgot the last one?" He knows I didn't.

"Right Time!"

"Now down to specifics. Right Product—was there any problem there?"

"Well, I did leave off the McPhees' ad stuffer."

"The right product cannot have missing parts. What about the Right Place?"

"I did miss some houses."

"Major shortfall in service for them. You won't know about delivering to wrong houses—why complain about a free paper? Leaving us, what?"

"Right Time."

"What time do customers get their papers for on-time delivery?"

"Before six o'clock. You know I didn't make that. I was still delivering at six-thirty when dinner started."

"And, if my timing from your last house is right, until nineteen minutes after that."

"I was so slow. I didn't know how to do anything!"

"Understandable. Even unavoidable. But isn't there more to the story? What happens when you stop and you spend time, as you say you did, introducing yourself and charming Mrs. Whoever and admiring her Siamese cat? Right Time goes more and more wrong. Am I right?"

Add confusion to my shame.

"But, Dad. Where People Mean Everything! 'Put people first and succeed,' you said, in those exact words! You made a big deal of this stuff, and it's the first thing about my business we talked about!"

1. **RIGHT** PRODUCT
2. **RIGHT** PLACE
3. **RIGHT** TIME

"Why do you suppose we talked about it first?"

"Because it's so important. It's the Service Promise."

"Yes, and it can't stand on its own. The promise dovetails with a high Service Standard you must strive to meet and exceed."

"Great, now you tell me!"

"What does *putting people first* mean, if you're not going to do what they pay you to do? Right Product. Right Place. Right Time."

"Not too much, I guess."

"You got that right. A lot of people who know better get just half of this. Either they try to get by on charm and personality without attention to the Service Standard. Or they only focus on that and forget about the person. It takes both!"

"I get it! They mean everything to me, and I have to deliver what means everything to them."

"Righter than right, Steve. And what do you suppose everything is, right now, to your father?"

"Product, Place, Time?"

"Did you hear that, Jan? We have raised another genius! I am thinking about the right dessert, which would be tonight's splendiferous apple crisp. Right here in front of me. Right this instant!"

Get Pedaling

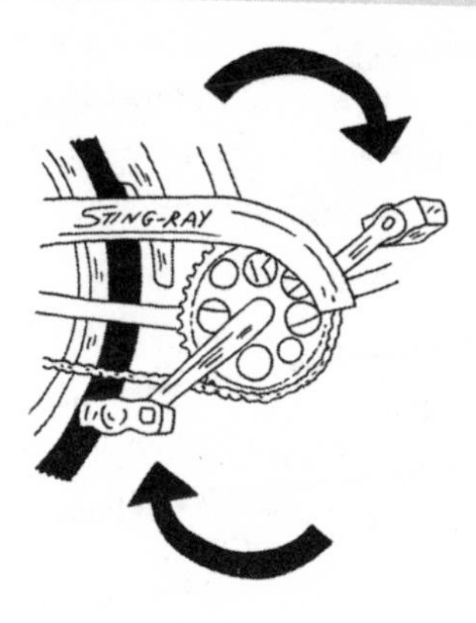

The Challenge

Define your own Service Standard. Right, Right, Right—each Right clearly and succinctly stated, doable, and in line with the expectations of the people to whom you make your Service Promise. Then strive to perform up to standard and exceed it when possible.

All Yours

Think of it as your own version of my boyhood *papers on porches by six o'clock.* Your words leave no wiggle room about the key, benchmark specifics of the standard and whether you meet it.

- Right Product. Specify the thing(s) you must provide in the course of your work—plated appetizers, professionally cleaned teeth, documentation, reports (either for the customer or others on your service team). Understand what makes a Right thing Right.

- Right Place. Whatever it is, there's somewhere it has to be, for somebody. With tangibles, this can be a physical place or places. With information or communication, the place might be digitally posted in the system or online, or sent to specific people, groups, and/or mass postings.
- Right Time. Date, hour, minute on calendar and clock, or time relative to a critical driving event—like, say, precise timing for prep before medical procedures or serving a banquet. There's a time that is right. And you need to know it.

Arbiters of Rightness

The people to whom you make your Service Promise set the bar for your Service Standard. The standard is your way of codifying what they want and expect, the better for you to serve them.

Not-Right Goes Wrong, Wrong, Wrong

The other day I experienced a three-way service fail.

I ordered five books online, and it could have been a perfect on-time delivery. Problem was, the driver dropped off the books out by the front gate on a day it was pouring rain. There was no rainproof bag on the box. The thing was mush when I found it, the books inside soaked. So much for Right Product. There went Right Time, too, because I had to wait to get the brand-new books I needed. Who even cared about Right Place?

This annoying event shows a typical domino effect. Blow one of your Rights, and more often than not, the other two go down with it.

Yes Harm, Yes Foul

Even minor, immediately correctable near-misses matter.

Let's say the server at a restaurant comes to your table with everybody's main courses, hot and perfectly plated, and puts food in front of the wrong people. Or hesitates and says, "Remind me, who has the rack of lamb, who has softshell crab?" Everything's still delicious, but service that should be seamless and correct isn't.

Not-Right always registers on some level.

Restaurants are, by the way, excellent living lessons in complicated, time-sensitive teamwork done to exacting standards. Food on the table involves a chain of Right, Right, Right going back to the kitchen. Back to the farm and the ocean, actually.

Super Right

Not long ago I got a surprise at-home visit from a dry cleaner bringing my freshly pressed-and-cleaned clothes. He asked if it would better if we arranged regular pickup and deliveries from home.

What do you think I said? And who has a loyal customer for life?

This is a brilliant example of a businessperson exceeding a service standard and, by so doing, killin' it.

Remember that Right is baseline. Strive for ways to make it Right-er.

Digitally Right

So much information is exchanged, and business relationships are built, remotely. Communication can be your Right Product, too. And getting it to the Right Place—in front of an attentive and receptive client, digitally—depends on getting there the right way, per each individual clients' preference. Could be email, text, messaging via social media or other means. Nothing but the right channel will get you where you want to be.

So...

What's your Right, Right, Right?

ANDERSON
BOY SCOUTS OF AMERICA

Chapter 3

When Priorities Collide

Scout Meeting Trauma

This is my first Boy Scouts of America shirt, but I am not the shirt's first scout. It served its purpose for a previous kid. Like my purple Sting-Ray, it ties into a family legacy and my new life after my twelfth birthday.

Starting seventeen years back, my big brothers joined the Boy Scouts of America at this same age and worked their way up to Eagle Scout, the highest attainable rank in BSA. Meanwhile, another male in our family also reached this pinnacle of scouting. But the story of Eagle Dad can wait.

As of now, I am officially on my way to being Anderson Eagle number five. Joining at age twelve and working all the way up to Eagle Scout is the third of the Parental Non-Negotiables.

After Eagle, and only after, I can get a Utah Driver License. This I know as surely as I sit in a church hall a couple blocks from home at my very first troop meeting.

I might be here anyway; scouting seems pretty cool. Being the kid I am, there's a good chance I'd go for Eagle, too. I don't know the other new scout who sits next to me, but it could be we'll both achieve the goal of goals in scouting and have back-to-back induction ceremonies. Or the other guy might lose interest and quit. Either way, I highly doubt he's in to win with no alternative to winning—which, I've got to be honest, I do not mind.

"Listen up," Mr. Bill the Scoutmaster says, and the room goes as silent as an undiscovered tomb. Mr. Bill speaks in a mild, quiet manner. A man of such size and obvious power, solid as a granite mountain and legendary expert in all things rugged and outdoorsy, does not have to raise his voice. If a focus group of twelve-year-old boys designed an ideal troop leader, he would be it.

After the formal BSA induction, things take a turn toward the traumatic when Mr. Bill briefly lays out what it takes to succeed in his troop. Top gotta-do is a once-a-month Friday night campout up in the Uinta Mountains.

"Rain or snow, warm out or five below like it was last week," Mr. Bill says, "you will learn the skills to be safe and comfortable and do more than survive in the wilderness. You will learn to love it. Freezing can be fun! Right, boys?"

Scouts hoot and fake-shiver. Mr. Bill gives a few more details about how, three Fridays from now, we have to be packed up to leave right after school and get back on Saturday.

The leader singles out a senior scout. "Gilchrist, you're working on the Reading merit badge. Remind the new scouts what *obligatory* means."

Per Gilchrist: If we are not in on the camping trips, we're off the track to advance up through the ranks and might as well get out of the troop.

The new guy next to me mouths, "Wow"—very excited and a titch scared. I hope that he can't see the despair and, I'll admit it, gut-freezing fear from the news about camping.

I can't do it. I just can't. There is no way.

No way and *Can't* and *Oh no* run through my head for the rest of the meeting.

Dinner of Doom, Mom of Gloom

And the bike ride home.

I would rather freeze all night in a blizzard in my undershorts, way up on one of Mr. Bill's mountains, than go back and say what must be said.

Freaking out makes me push the bike to terminal velocity so I get where I don't want to go in half the time. Then, wouldn't you know, Dad is home already. He and Mom are together.

"Well, how's the new scout?"

Mom smiles and looks for positivity. "Is anything wrong?"

"I'm fine. Sorry, I have to get to my room."

I know they know something is amiss, and it will all come out at dinner.

Never have I wished so hard for the prayer to run extra-long and then for silent hunger-killer eating to go into multiple overtime. My sisters, who are clairvoyant about trouble, seem to know something's up even before Dad, upbeat as ever, asks how the first troop meeting went.

"Horrible. Just horrible."

Silence. Mom gets up to do something in the kitchen.

More tortuous silence, and I spill.

"I can't do it. I really can't. Mr. Bill says I have to go on the Friday night campouts. They're once a month and if I can't go…" Dad cocks his head and dials down to a 10 percent smile.

"I went to a few of those campouts myself with your brothers. Fun…"

"But I have the paper route, too. I have to deliver the papers on Friday!"

"Do you?"

"And if I'm gone I can't do delivery."

"True, you can't."

"I'm not going to do it."

"What aren't you going to do?" Dad asks with gentle patience.

"It's impossible. Dad, I can't do Boy Scouts!"

Way over the line, way too close to tears. Nobody so far as I know has openly challenged a Non-Negotiable. What choice do I have, though? I fear the consequences, feel mortified at letting down my parents, and hate crashing and burning in front of my sisters.

Mom comes back bearing dessert.

"Will you look at that? Rice pudding! My absolute favorite!" Nice try, Dad. But he cannot stop the other thing that Mom brings besides dessert. He, like everybody else, fears what remains famous in the family as the Three M's.

Mom's Moments of Misery—more miserable for us than for her by orders of magnitude. No one wants to let down or upset Mom. Ever. The basic deal is that if you make her feel bad, you will feel a million times worse. Bystanders will also feel deeply ashamed, if not at least a little bit sorry they were born. It's a true gift. She doesn't say a word but does it with her face and, somehow, her entire being. If she's disappointed, you are paralyzed by guilt, clinically depressed, crushed and plunged into the bottomless abyss where no light has ever shined.

This time, obviously, I am the major disappointer. Anybody who knows a thing about Boy Scouting, especially at pinnacle Eagle Scout level, knows that a mother has major skin in the game. The big stuff depends on her buy-in and assistance. After heavy maternal investment in three Eagle Scout sons, Mom fully intends to go out on one last win with one last Eagle—the son who just said he won't be a scout because he can't.

Help me. Somebody. Anybody.

Solution Sought, Found

What seems like throwing me a lifeline may be Dad saving himself. It is in his interest to Socrates me to some kind of acceptable resolution.

Mom's interest, too—for us to feel so horrible, she must feel pretty bad.

"You know," Dad says, "now that we have rice pudding—which is absolutely delicious!—we might want to re-think. It sounds like camping out is important."

"If I skip it to do my paper route, I can't advance. Why bother?"

"No camp-out, no Eagle. Am I getting that right?"

"Yes, Dad."

"I think I understand the dilemma. You can't be two places at once."

Dad totally gets it, and now I'm feeling some hope. If I can't be both a paperboy and a Boy Scout, one of them can't be a Non-Negotiable anymore. Something's gotta give, right?

"Remind me again, Steve, who has to do your paper route once a month on Friday?"

"We've been through this, Dad. Papers on all the porches by six, and everything. My Service Standard. Right, Right, Right is all on me!"

"Your responsibility and nobody else's? Yes?"

"Yesssss." I hiss it out like a snake because, you know, where's he going?

"Again, Steve, where do you fit in?"

"Well, my job is the Right, Right, Right."

“Hmmmm,” he says, looking into the Dad dimension like he’s thinking out loud. “Your responsibility, yes, but who decides if it’s your job on a day-to-day basis?”

“Ummm, I do?”

“Excellent! Your service standard is your responsibility. Who does each task, to deliver on the promise, is also your responsibility, but not always, and not necessarily, your job.”

My face says “Huh?”

“Let’s see, who writes and edits the news that goes in the paper? Up to standard and on time, so it’s in good shape to print.”

“A bunch of news people.”

“Who drops off the papers every day, on time in the expected place?”

“Different guys. They just show up.”

“Well, who did the paper route when your brothers got sick or hurt or we had to go out of town for funerals and what have you?”

“Guys they knew, or maybe open-route boys.”

“Who took responsibility to make those arrangements so the job got done?”

“My brothers did.”

“Who runs into this sort of thing all day long at his office, and sometimes wants to tear out his hair when people throw their hands up and say something can't be done? Why? Because they don't slow down and sort things out!"

"You do?"

"Who sometimes feels profound exasperation because grown people create great big and entirely false dilemmas and give themselves a simple, easy way out which is… which is what?"

"They say they can't do it."

"Exactly! Does that sound familiar? Any false dilemmas at the table? Conflicts that didn't conflict?"

"I feel so dumb. I didn't think…"

Dad smiles and grasps my shoulder. "Not dumb, Steven. Human. And young. And upset. Upset people don't see solutions that are staring them in the face. Happens all the time."

"I just completely freaked out, because I really, really want to go camping next month. In the snow! But I need to keep my paper route, too."

"Well, you just made a plan to do both, didn't you?"

"I had some help, Dad."

"More important, you found that you have other sources of help. You can see to it that your papers get delivered. Or, if you insist on doing that, I suppose you could line somebody up to go camping for you."

"No way that's going to happen, Dad."

EAGLE SCOUT
BOY SCOUTS OF AMERICA
BE PREPARED
ANDERSON
BOY SCOUTS OF AMERICA
SALT LAKE

"So, one night a month you have a high-priority, necessary task only you are qualified to perform. Your job, as you say. Which is freezing your nether parts in the middle of nowhere."

"Arthur!"

"And at the same time, you do Right, Right, Right by your customers by ensuring that they get their papers."

"That's it, Dad."

"Can you be two places at once?"

"Of course not."

"Do you have to be?"

"No, I don't."

"And you, my son, now know something that some grownups never learn."

I do know. This is the first and last time Non-Negotiables, my highest priorities, hit head-on—or seem to, because of course they really don't. Some names of guys I can trust to do my route once a month jump into my head. It all works out!

And praise be, MMM has left the room. Mom shines happiness and love on her Eagle-to-be-if-she-has-anything-to-do-with-it. As she surely will.

"Jan, any chance of seconds on my favorite dessert?"

I get more, too. Somewhere in here I ate my pudding but did not taste a thing.

Get Pedaling

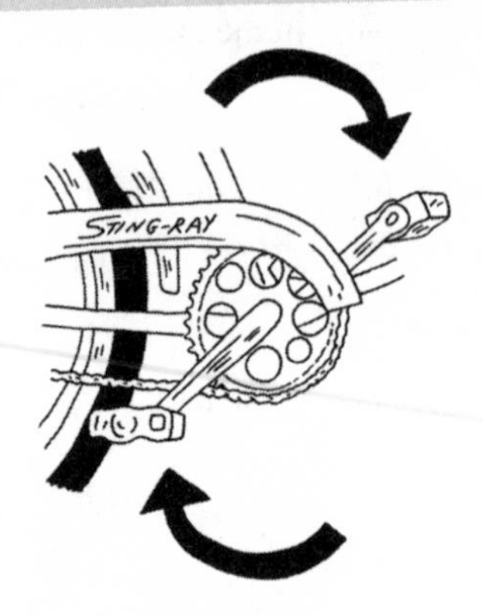

The Challenge

Sort out priorities at work that seem to collide but probably don't. Do it by delineating between tasks that really are narrowly yours to perform—i.e., your job—and those where you may be accountable for results but don't necessarily need to do them yourself.

Know who has your back, who can perform priority tasks and achieve desired results in the shared mission to meet your Service Standard and serve your team's customers.

Okay, Maybe It Is Your Job

If professional certification, licensing and/or special expertise and experience are involved, it may be. You might be the only qualified welder on your repair shop team, so if that's what is needed, you're it! Ditto if you're the only state-licensed registered hygienist on a dental practice team. Unlicensed teammates cannot step in and clean teeth.

Or It Really Isn't

Chances are, though, that lines between team members and who does what are more about mindset and established routine than reality. Then the lines may need to be erased, the better to keep the team's Service Promise.

Beware what we call the Silo Mentality. This is a narrow, vertical, even jealous conception of specific tasks tied to specific people, as in saying/thinking things like…

A. It's not my job, and I won't do it.

B. It's my job, and nobody else can do it because it's mine.

Either one can cause upset and create confusion, like twelve-year-old me freaking out because I imagined that I, and nobody else, had to deliver the papers every fourth Friday.

Knock Down Those Silos

Focus first on what has to happen to deliver on your Service Promise and your Service Standard.

Root Meanings

Understand a couple key results- and task-related words in terms of roots they contain. It helps clarify thinking.

Accountable: This indicates a result that can and will be counted for or against your performance and, therefore, you. You may or may not have to perform every task, but you will be judged by the end result.

Responsible: Here there's a response you're called on to make, by performing a task that yields certain results, as in "job responsibilities."

For example, it's everyone's responsibility to create customers and generate new business, with individual responsibilities for tasks that serve the overall mission. The marketing director is accountable, and is measured by, new customer acquisition and overall marketing results. To that end, others have their jobs to do.

Okay, Who Has Your Back?

Do an inventory of your total service team, immediate and extended. Who is positioned to step in when the need arises? Who can you step in for?

Especially where special expertise and training is involved, the resources may be outside the team, in temp services or recent retirees.

Look, too, at in-house physical resources, equipment that can be subbed-in to cover your you-know-what.

Make a Plan

Know how to utilize the resources you have just identified. Prepare for the unexpected—with no change in the team's Service Promise and the needed results it entails.

The Best Plan: Everybody Has Everybody's Back

Smart teams do themselves huge favors by cross-training team members to cover for each other. This encourages a general got-your-back mentality and willingness to pitch in.

No, You Don't Want to Be Indispensable

And nobody else wants you to be that way either. There is weakness, not power and job security, in being the only one who can do what you do. And no team should depend on one member.

So...

It takes a team to win. Who is on yours?

BANK
Where
Mean Everything
People

Chapter 4

When People Don't Mean Everything

Major Money

Could be beginner's luck or that paper routes, like so many things in life, have honeymoon periods where everybody tries hard to make great impressions that don't always last. Whatever the reason, my first collection month turns out to be a breeze. And I am blissfully unaware there might be future challenges and drama collecting money from every last one of the people who owe me.

Don't get me wrong, the great majority will be rock solid for as long as I have the route. But note the "owe me." Once a month I personally bill seventy-some customers, and they pay cash or write checks made out to me. I owe the company for papers delivered, whether or not I collect for them. Once again I look back and salute the folks in the paper's business office who devised a can't-lose deal. For themselves.

I, the twelve-year-old, am hugely impressed with my first-ever monthly gross receipts. Never have I had so much money in hand. As an early adolescent business nerd, this pleases me more than money that's mine to spend because it's cash flow for my own independent enterprise.

Big-dealness goes up as I push the stack of checks and paper money into a manila envelope. I re-check my entries and total on the printed form for recording collections. And then I fill out one of the personalized bank deposit slips that just came in the mail. This is the day's big-deal Golden Ticket. I mean, look whose name is on it!

Freezing rain will not stop me from going to First National Bank to make my first deposit on my personal business vehicle. I pedal the bike with extreme caution, feeling often for the envelope stuffed into my puffy ski jacket. I arrive all in one piece and park the bike under Dad's immortal words: Where People Mean Everything.

Hello, First National. It's me, Steve. Mr. Everything has arrived!

Mr. Invisible

I take a deep breath of warm indoor air and stride with confidence, Dad-style, toward the tellers' windows. It would be nice to get another executive personal greeting, but this is just routine banking. I don't mind that no one so much as looks up from the desks next to the lobby. These people keep their heads down and work on behalf of me, a valued client, supervised by bosses in private offices with windows and glass doors, including my very own good friend Jane. It would be bad form to wave at her, so I keep striding, loving my bank's hum of purpose, gaining imaginary height with every step.

The afternoon slow period coupled with the horrible weather makes me the only customer, but the tellers at windows all look busy. The woman I pick counts money, eyes on the green like I'm not here. She finishes and looks at the space I occupy. And I'm still not here! She fails to register my presence until I give her no choice by clearing my throat.

"May I help you?" she asks in a cold way that knocks inches off my height.

"I, I..."

"Yes?"

"I'd like to make a deposit. Please."

"You would, would you? What do you have to deposit?"

My stack of checks and currency ought to turn her around.

Except no. "Where did you get all this?"

"They're mine."

"They are, are they?"

"Mine for my account."

Now I'm annoyed. Those are ugly drugstore-looking glasses you're wearing, lady. I don't like the chain they're on, either.

In my mind's eye, I cut the same figure as I did with Dad—as Dad himself in his Mr. Mac masterpiece. Just like him, I come dressed for my profession. Except, unlike Dad, my work clothes consist of a ski jacket smudged with ink from fresh-printed newspapers, stocking cap smudged from wiping inky hands on it, after-school jeans and sneakers wrong for the weather but right for riding. Though I try hard to carry myself with poise and confidence far beyond my years, my baby face says I could be much younger.

But, you know, my clothes are righter on me than the so-so suit on the manager the teller calls over and confers with in a hush. They flip through my money and then turn to me.

"Where did you get all this, young man?"

"Who gave this to you?"

"Where did you find it?"

The inquisition brings on an attack of what I now call *authority tremor*—shakiness and shrinkage of one's entire being brought on by someone in command, or who wants to be and gets kicks out of humiliating others. I want to apologize and belly-crawl to the door, except I'm also furious that they demean me when it's my money!

"I have a paper route and just did my collections for the month."

"Well, now we're getting somewhere. Why didn't you just say so? You can come back and open an account with a grownup."

"Like I said, I already have an account."

Don't you two geniuses have a slip with the account number on it? Where else would a deposit go? The rest should be simple, except they don't find the account until I think to tell them to look under Arthur S. Anderson because we have—duh—a joint account, also on the deposit slip. When they finally find it, they owe me a huge "We are so, so sorry, Mr. Anderson…"

Instead I get goodbye snark, like I should clearly state my business next time. The suit asks if there's anything else they can do for me.

"Yes, I'd like to see Jane."

Didn't see this coming, did you?

"Jane who? This is a big bank."

"Jane the New Accounts Manager. We know each other."

"I am sure you do. Is she expecting you?"

He tells me to make an appointment next time, and the teller closes her window.

If wounds to the ego damaged the body, I'd go out on a stretcher, apoplectic with rage. On the way to the doors I see Jane in her office. She stares blankly into the dimension where people gaze during long phone calls, eyes in my general direction. No surprise while she's on the phone that I'm invisible. But then she hangs up and I wave, and the face is still blank. I'm not here, and I am absolutely not Everything to anybody in this place.

```
Memo

From: Mr. Invisible

To: First National Bank

You blew it, and you will
miss me. I am never coming
back.
```

Anger Diffused, Saved By Pie

Of all my paper route memories, this comes back vividly and strongest of all in terms of feeling. Whenever I remember what happened, I'm that humiliated, angry kid all over again.

I walk out of the bank mad; do my route on foot—it's now too icy to bike—mad; totter home like a ninety-year-old so I don't break my neck mad. Then I sit at the table and fume, seethe, fulminate while poking at a dinner that's one of my favorites. Everything Mom makes is a favorite, actually, even if I never had it before. But deliciousness does not matter when I am so mad.

Dad opens the table talk with some back-and-forth with my sisters, then turns to me.

"You're barely eating, Steve. Are you upset about something?"

"Where People Mean Everything. Hah!" I burst out. "You need to go that bank and take back your slogan."

"Ah," says Dad, "you must have gone in after school. Did something happen?"

It all comes out with full-blast fury, no Q&A needed. Then, in the usual mild, interested manner—can't he just blow up about those jerks, like me?—he sighs.

"You know, if that's the customer experience, they might be better off without the slogan. Sometimes no marketing, no advertising, no promotion is better than the most creative high-impact campaign. Sometimes doing nothing is better."

Odd to hear that from our in-house famous advertising man. "What do you mean?"

"When the experience falls short, and a business does not live up to its words and the image it projects, the damage can be more serious than any amount of advertising can repair."

"I know. It happened to me today."

"That's not quite what I mean. Bad customer experience can be infuriating. But customers can take their business elsewhere and tell everyone else what went wrong. A business that talks loudly but fails to walk the talk can fail, period."

"Good. First National deserves to!"

"Easy, Tiger. That bank helps keep my company in business and helps put food on this table. But there's something else to consider.

"Ask yourself, Steve: Were you more upset about what happened today than you were happy about the red-carpet treatment when you opened the account?"

"Absolutely, Dad. I don't ever want to go back!"

Dad lights up and proclaims, "Good! That makes you a normal human being and a typical customer or client. Let people down, and they feel the experience deeply. They want to spread the bad news, which travels farther, faster, and hits harder than good news ever will. Speaking to you, who are now in business, what don't you want to do?"

"I don't ever want anybody to have the kind of experience I just had."

"Exactly. You get the point. You went to the place Where People Mean Everything. But you went at a moment when a couple of employees fell far short. That's the "When," Steve—the variable—which was your customer interaction."

"I get it."

"You must constantly stay on top and…" He waits for me.

"I need to live up to the Service Promise and Service Standard."

"When? How many times?"

"Always. Every time."

"Right you are!"

Bless you, Mom, for bringing in pie. Happy Dad and no more Socrates.

Get Pedaling

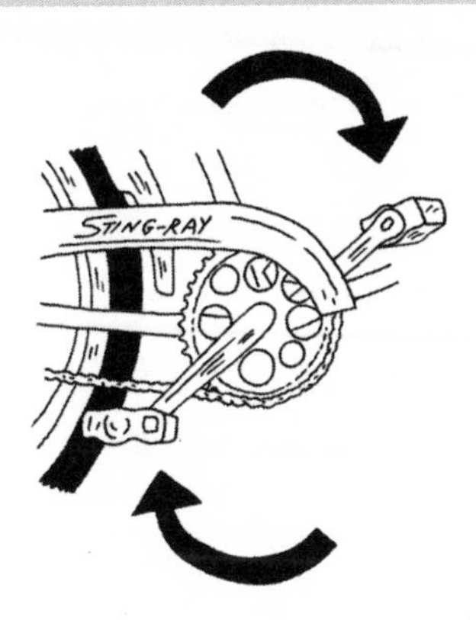

The Challenge

Make every encounter with present and potential clients opportunities to live up to your Service Promise.

Make it happen at all points of engagement at every stage of the customer relationship. For all members of your team, train in attitudes and responses to deliver on the Promise and make people glad they're doing business with you.

Task One

Identify each and every point of engagement where your Service Promise comes into play before, during, and after the purchase experience.

Educating the Team

Each point of engagement will involve an encounter with specific members of your service team. It may be in person, in a call, or electronically. Each encounter has a purpose and can improve or detract from the customer experience.

Know who on the service team is part of each encounter and train them in Right, Right, Right outcomes within the encounter, while honoring the Promise.

What about Teammates Who Never Deal with People?

Everybody on the team has to be educated and on board.

The Service Promise and Service Standard apply to internal interactions with fellow team members as much as they do external contacts. That's all part of organization culture, which gets a complete treatment in my book *The Culture of Success*.

Right, Right, Right, Right

Instead of asking yourself, "What do I do to serve *this customer*?" ask, "How can I help *this person* get what they *want*?"

There's almost always something that's a bigger deal than the service people pay for. Having delivered, per your Service Standard, it's on you to help them get what they want.

Consider this your fourth Right after the original three: Product, Place, and Time.

What They Really Want

What does a master athlete with runner's knee want from the orthopedic surgeon? It is not surgery. The want is to regain painless mobility and, hopefully, a return to regular runs.

Nobody wants a dental procedure, but everybody wants a beautiful smile. People don't buy a book for words on pages, but for the diversion and beauty to be found within. Great food is, of course, key to a great restaurant experience, but the desired result may be bonding with others at the table.

So, what do your customers really want?

Everybody Is Somebody

People want to feel important to the service team and feel that the business they bring is important. This means that every team member knows how to show respect and recognition and does so at each and every contact.

This chapter begins with a case study of a service fail on the part of two people at the tellers' counter at First National Bank. They treated ink-stained twelve-year-old me as a nobody even though I was, in fact, a bank customer. In so doing, they betrayed the bank's Where People Mean Everything Service Promise.

Okay, maybe I did not qualify in their eyes as People. But that still would have been a fail even if I were I a kid off the street with no legit bank business. A little politeness and kind interest would have done credit to First National and themselves.

What's So Bad about Bad

Blame human nature. People just naturally go to the dark side of experience. Bad news travels far, at light speed. This applies to bad customer experience. People obsess about it and tell everybody, and their brothers and sisters, about it over and over. "You're not going to believe what happened…" they say. And others do believe it. Bad business has consequences. The price is still higher when a business fails to deliver on its promises.

So…

What's your strategy for delivering on your Service Promise and Service Standard at every point of engagement?

WELCOME

Chapter 5

More Than Right

Dialing It In

Wherever I point my eyes, the bike really wants to go.

There's a lesson here for when we're not on wheels, too. Where we look can determine our direction in life.

But at age twelve it's all about the Sting-Ray and me. I have to work hard to de-link my eyes and steering and pedal straight while looking sideways to pitch papers onto porches. This does not come naturally. Nor does keeping up sufficient speed so the bike remains stable.

Let us not forget the challenge of steering with heavily-loaded handlebars, left hand only so I can throw papers with my right. Fortunately, I get plenty of practice. Seventy or so houses on the route makes 2,100 ride-by paper pitches in a month. Coming into Month Two, I get more and more dialed-in and have fun like this is my own private sport. There should be competitions for this stuff.

I throw to a strike zone on the front porch with a sidearm snap like tossing a frisbee. I spin my rolled-up papers horizontally so they hit the porch and come in for a sliding stop. Vertical end-over-end, the papers keep hopping to who knows where.

For complete coverage as I go, no doubling back, I zig-zag back and forth across streets. Most households take the paper, so I can have a dozen or more zigs and zags per block. Meanwhile, I watch to avoid getting hit by cars and not hit humans/dogs/cats and random stuff in my path.

My favorite fine points, requiring the most practice and finesse, involve launching the paper to the target zone. I depend on backhand as much as my forehand toss because I hit houses both left and right. Both ways, I have to take my shot with both accuracy and proper force. Too much oomph and the paper bangs into the door, maybe leaves a ding if it's aluminum. Too little, I have to double back, park, pick up the paper and play the short game.

The more I do it, the more consistent I get. But even immortals of the pitcher's mound give up home runs and unintentional walks.

Oh Yeah, Oh No

Five weeks into my paperboy-ing, it's a glorious day that has people out in shorts yelling about spring. Everybody knows winter will take more shots at SLC. But why even think about end-of-season snowfall today? And why not ride my route wearing an aspirational t-shirt that's more about how warm I want it to be than how not-quite it actually is.

Why not, while I'm at it, be my own greatest fan for riding and paper-throwing skills on my career-best day? No doubt about it, this Anderson kid is a phenom, a natural.

Oh yeah.

Still, I do not lose respect for the trickiest delivery on my route. You can't really call the narrow landing between the steps and the door a porch. It's just a strip of what used to be the porch before a remodel created an enclosed mini-patio outside the original front door.

Even after I regularly scored at other houses, I would go close to place the paper because it's easier than picking it up from wherever it bounced or fell short. But then I started having a little success.

Today of all days, I have absolutely no doubt I will.I will…

No, that didn't just happen…

But it did…

Oh no.

Who knows why, I put way too much heat on the paper and it goes a little bit wide of the door. Bad luck plays a role. I mean, the paper could go wider and miss altogether, or it could hit the door. Flying more slowly, it might not break anything. But the paper hits end-on like an anti-window weapon and smashes through a skinny vertical pane of glass next to the door. It lands in what would be a pretty good spot if there were no enclosure. Then there wouldn't be broken glass, and I wouldn't get off the bike and stand like a memorial statue of myself after I die too young of shock.

Only a kid who prides himself on being good and does something bad can feel such terror. It's all out of proportion to actual badness and possible consequences. Even the idea that people will yell at me seems unbearable. I take slow steps to ring the doorbell to face my inexorable fate.

A mom-looking woman, neither young nor old, comes to the inner door with a "Who's this?" face that changes when she sees what happened and says, "Oh my."

I blurt out "Sorry!" multiple ways, babble about not knowing how this happened, say I'll pay every cent for repairs, time, and trouble.

Amazingly not angry, the lady says, "I'm kind of surprised it hasn't happened before, with all this glass. And I know you will cover the damages."

"Absolutely! I can leave the bike for security."

"No need to leave anything. You're a good boy, I can tell. You did a brave thing, marching up to the bell and ringing. Your parents should be pleased."

I insist, or try to insist, that I clean up the broken glass, but she won't have it. "It'll only take a minute. Looks like you've still got papers to deliver."

I leave kinda shocked about life as I know it not ending, thanks to the lady being so civilized and me being such a good kid. Or lucky I broke a nice person's window. Or my own fault because I got carried away and thought I was big stuff. Or something.

I pitch papers extra carefully for the rest of the route.

The Least I Could Do

Dad may have something in mind for a dinner table symposium. We'll never know because I bring up the broken window. Mom looks up with concern, Dad with interest. My sisters show interest, too, but more like sharks sensing blood in the water.

"Why, do you suppose?" Dad muses.

"I went over it and over it—it just happened."

"Things do, with thrown projectiles."

He Q&As through what I did in response to the accident, and what the woman said and did and how I left it. Replaying it, I feel more like the good kid she says I am and even kinda proud, unforced throwing error aside.

"The least you could do, under the circumstances, right?"

"Yes."

"In spite of the mishap, she was satisfied with your sincere apology, your attitude, and assurances that you will make good on her loss."

"She really was."

"A satisfied customer, am I right?"

"I'm pretty sure."

"Not bad, Steve. You made a solid, honest start. But let's think a minute. Did you get to a place Where People Mean Everything? Or did you miss a valuable opportunity to do better—even better than if they got their paper in the right place on time as promised?"

"Better than Right, Right, Right? Because I smashed a window?"

"It can happen, if you do what it takes to make it happen. Remember what I said, 'The least you could do?'"

"Sure, and I did."

"What if you did more, much more than people need to be satisfied, more than they'd ever expect."

"Like what?

"We'll get to that in a minute..."

And the Most

Why can't he just tell me stuff, even yell it at me like other dads? Instead of Qs & As that go all over and, on nights like this, hurt my head?

"What, do we suppose, is the best, most valuable kind of customer?"

"Like you said a minute ago, a satisfied customer."

"What if there's a better kind? And unexpected problems like your broken window give you a chance to create that kind. I mean a *loyal* customer."

"Aren't they the same?"

"There's overlap; but no, they are not the same."

My face, as it often does, goes "Huh?"

"Think about this, Steve, and you'll understand why loyalty does more for you and your business: Satisfied customers are not always loyal..."

He lets that sink in and says, "And loyal customers are not always satisfied."

"How can not-satisfied be better?"

"Well, because they're still loyal when things go wrong, and they stick with you. Satisfied customers are just that, satisfied. No more, no less. You meet expectations and give them their money's worth. But if something goes wrong or they just don't feel like sticking, goodbye."

"What makes the loyal ones stick?"

"They know if something goes wrong, you will make things right—more than right—by doing more and exceeding expectations. That's what's called making a Great Recovery."

"How do they know that?"

"Well, in this case, because you are about to make a Great Recovery after throwing a newspaper through their window!"

"Now?"

"Would now exceed expectations?"

He Socrates-es me through an immediate plan of action. I will personally tell my customers that tomorrow upon opening, Bennett's Window and Glass will be contacted to make complete repairs, paid direct from my end. I will tell them in person, right away, and present a note of apology and thanks for being such understanding, great customers.

"Is this a Good Recovery, Steve?"

"Sure."

"Well, I would call it a Great Recovery. Never settle for less than great. Good is not good enough if you want customer loyalty."

Dad says to Mom, "Jan, can you think of anything else to send along to sweeten the deal?"

He knows, as we all do, that Mom maintains a constant supply of famously excellent home-baked cookies for family use, hospitality to walk-in visitors, and unplanned gifting. She keeps a big jar in the kitchen fresh and full for emergency use, like a feel-good fire extinguisher.

"Today we have oatmeal chocolate chip."

"If word gets out, everybody will want broken windows."

"Speaking of that," I say, "Should I?"

"Should you what?"

"Should I break everybody's windows to have Great Recoveries and make everybody loyal?"

"Now there's a thought. Run the numbers on repairs. Think about your reputation as a delivery boy, too. That could have a detrimental effect on jobs and future income. This might not pencil out, Steve. Now then, don't you have a Great Recovery note to write?"

"But dessert…"

"We'll save some for you. Unless it's so good I have to take seconds and thirds!"

Get Pedaling

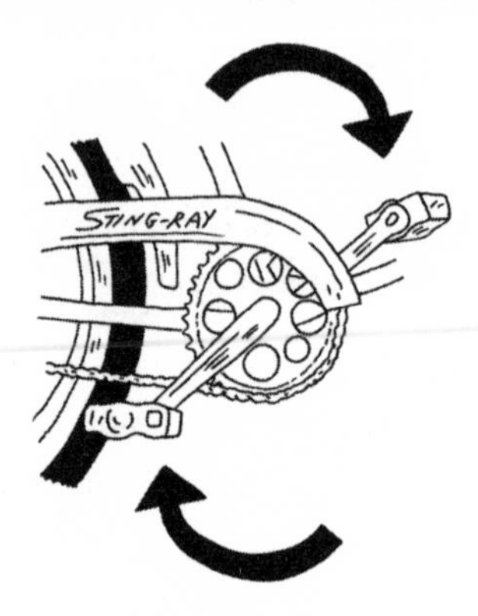

The Challenge

Make plans for what to do for customers when things don't go as planned, and make Great Recoveries when your service falls short. Always do more than just make good on service lapses and customer disappointments.

Exceed expectations in such a way as to create customer loyalty, which is more lasting and valuable than satisfaction.

Never be satisfied with satisfaction again!

Loyalty Test

Loyalty is truly the gold standard of customer relations. It means you're the go-to for people who identify as your customers. You may be a braggable asset to them, with referrals and online reviews yours for the asking. If things go sideways, as they're known to do, loyal customers are likely to give you the benefit of the doubt and stick with you.

It seems counterintuitive, but you can earn loyalty for the first time when all or part of Right, Right, Right service goes wrong. Here's your opportunity to step up and exceed expectations in a memorable, amazing manner with a Great Recovery that does more than make good.

Satisfaction, by contrast, is transactional. Deals are one-offs. Things are fine 'til they're not. Then it's *hasta la vista* to you.

More than Making People Whole

Never stop with conventional remedies to make things right—refunds, credits, replacements, loaners, and the like. You may have a box here to check, but it won't get more than lukewarm satisfaction, because everybody does pretty much the same.

Leave the pack behind by doing more in a unique way.

More Is Fair

The woman whose window I smashed would have been satisfied with money to cover repairs. But that would not have been fair compensation for a problem of my making. She'd still have lost time and been inconvenienced by lining up the repair, paying for it, and waiting to be repaid.

My deal, to take care of everything and pay directly, went beyond the norm. But it was only fair.

And that was still not good enough. The idea is to be more than fair.

Sweetener

Do it with extras, including a signature compensatory add-on that seems personal and from the heart.

My smashed window people got a same-night visit and apology, a personal note, and a literally sweet sweetener, a plate of Mom's amazing cookies. Which do you think made the biggest impression? I'll bet the farm it was the cookies. Why? Because, well, cookies!

Personal, delicious, neighbor to neighbor.

Proportional, Appropriate

Make your Great Recovery memorable, worth telling friends about and showing you in a positive light.

Give people reasons to feel that they get more out of the unfortunate situation than they lose. And that there's nothing, or next to nothing, left to feel bad about.

Keep things proportional. Too little can be insulting. Too much is wrong, too. Had such a thing been possible, it would not have been right to give my broken window people a new car.

Create a connection with the service incident. What you give will seem appropriate to what they didn't get. It could be perfectly right to give a note and coffee card after an optometrist appointment runs late. Do not, however, give new tires to a couple whose hotel suite was not available because of burst pipes or overbooking, even if the tires are in the same price ballpark as the suite.

Recovery Theater

Let's say a mistake is made during dinner at a famously good restaurant. It's not enough to spoil the meal, but management does not want it to define the experience. Or, heaven forbid, generate negative buzz.

Things will come off the tab, of course. But that, with nothing else, might feel like awarding damages. What's needed is some feel-good theater.

Maybe, after the main courses, the sous chef comes to the table with plates of a special dessert he created, to be debuted next week. This group will be the first to taste! To dial up the aren't-we-special vibe, he asks for opinions. Or the manager comes with the plates, compliments of the chef, and has similar foodie blah-blah-blah. The experience is a fresh reminder of why this place is a great choice. And the people at the table have something new and cool to talk about.

"Sorry" Is Never Where You End

"Sorry" is where you start, after the regrettable swing-and-miss in service. Say it and mean it, with recognition that this could be a major disappointment for people. But don't overdo it. "Sorry" said too many times is dangerous. It fixes attention on what went wrong and says there's a lot to be sorry for.

Do your best to lift the mood. Make the loss a customer relations win by showing how you and your team bend over backwards to do right by your people no matter what. The point, as in the old showbiz adage, is to leave them wanting more.

So…

What's your Great Recovery plan?

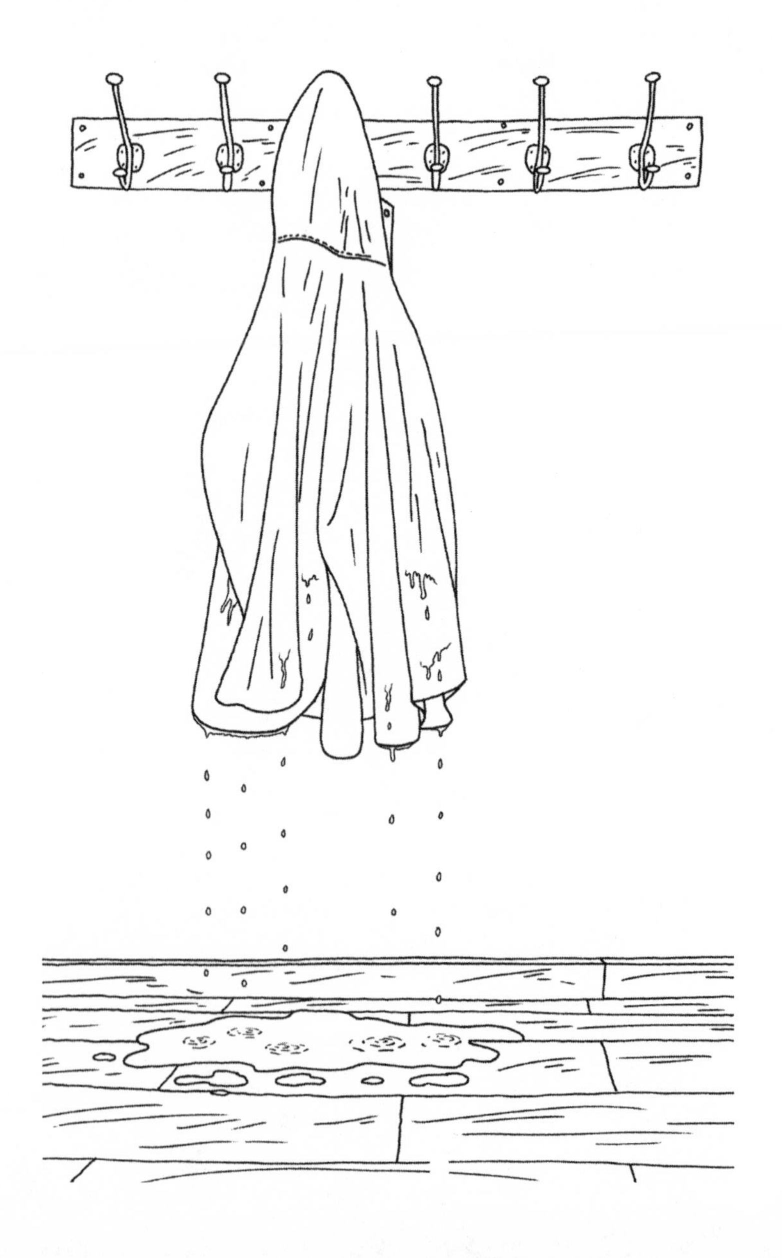

Chapter 6

Everything For Everybody

Soggy Saturday

Grass and flowers will love this Saturday morning of slashing rain. The kid squishing around the neighborhood in waterlogged sneakers, not so much.

My Boy Scout rain poncho flaps all over in wind gusts, so the purple Sting-Ray stays in the garage for my monthly in-person collections. Most customers have already paid using envelopes rubber-stamped with my address that go out with my papers. Some mail in checks, some leave the envelopes out for me to pick up. A few customers happen to see me on the route and settle. The rest of the money I go out and get. In 1978, none of this is auto-pay, auto-entered, auto-anything. Receivables show up various ways, at various times, in varying amounts, all tracked and tallied on paper.

One bell I always ring belongs to Mrs. Viola Taylor, in her late eighties and living alone. I don't mind that it takes her quite a while to get to the door and that I always have to tell her how much she owes and wait while she counts out a couple dollar bills and pokes through coins poured out of a jar.

The Hutchinsons come next, a surprise because they usually mail right away. I don't think we've ever actually met until now. Mrs. Hutchinson seems young to look so worn and worried.

She gives me the payment envelope and says, "I wanted to see you in person. We have a little problem."

She explains that she's still at work when the paper comes and her husband has a hard time getting around.

"Pete can't get in and out of the front door on his own until his brother comes and builds a little ramp. He might not go out to get the paper anyway because he hates being seen in that wheelchair."

"How can I help?"

"If you put the paper through the mail slot, we have a little table right on the other side. He's stir crazy with no work and the news is something to look forward to."

"Happy to do it."

A little voice in my head says I'll have to lay down the bike with an almost-full load of papers and walk up on the porch. This will slow me down, for sure. But, you know, for one customer who is obviously hurting, I am more than happy.

Lowell and the Dragon Lady

One guy slaps his forehead, says he forgot the envelope on his desk, and gives it to me. After that come an out-of-town-and-forgot, a couple of plain old sorrys, and some not-at-homes that seem inexplicable. Where on earth did they go on a morning like this?

One doorbell brings a burly man with a moustache who yells back into the house, "Lock up our daughters and the valuables, Martha; it's an Anderson!" He grins down at me and says, "You, Steven, should be eternally grateful your looks favor your mother's side. Tell her I say so."

"Hello, Mr. Everett. I'll be sure to tell Dad, too."

"I'll tell him myself. You may salute and call me sir!"

Not yet, but in a few years, I'll be able to give at least a little of what I get from Lowell Everett, a buddy of Dad's going back to their Army days and legendary figure in oft-told war stories.

"Before I pay you for that fish wrap they call a newspaper," he says, "I want to, all kidding aside, bring up something about delivery. The weather made me think of it."

He points out that he, on his side of the screen door, is dry while I, out on the porch, get more and more soaked. He also says the paper generally lands about where I'm standing. He really appreciates the way I plastic the paper to keep it dry, but…

"What happens to me when I come out to get it?"

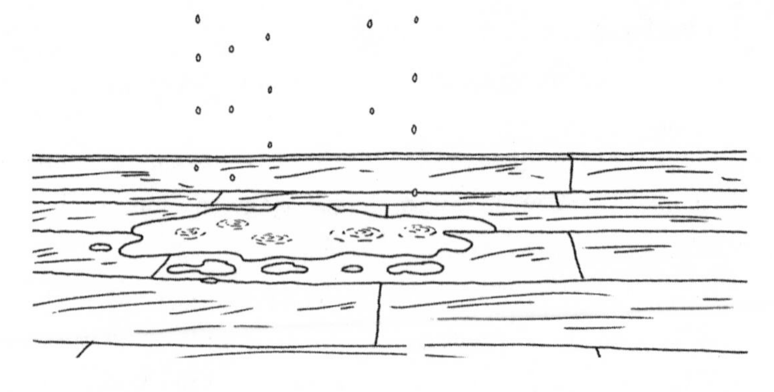

"You get a little bit wet?"

"More than a little in a gulley washer like this. Now, do you want to be a hero, be a gung-ho soldier like your old man used to be? Still is, actually."

"Umm, I don't know."

"Put the paper inside the screen door when it's raining. Tomorrow's supposed to be another wet one. Monday, too. Step up and do your duty, soldier! Think about it."

"Yes, sir! I will think about it, sir!"

And he barks, "Dismissed!"

Since it's Legendary Lowell and this military stuff is one of a hundred ways he goofs around, and since I believe he's serious about putting the papers inside the screen doors, I do think about it. That stops when I get to the house of a woman with a cigarette who blows smoke out of her nose like a dragon.

“Who are you and what do you want?”

After I tell her she snarls, “So you’re the one who brings the paper after I go to work every afternoon. Here’s some news, newsboy, if you don’t get it me to me by three o’clock, I will raise Cain downtown!”

Dragon Lady, name on my list Monica Dunbar, drags on her cigarette and coughs while I explain she actually gets the paper earlier than most people because of where her house is.

“If I wanted a story, I’d look at your lousy paper. I want it in time to take it to work, as I was explicitly promised. Or I will cancel my subscription and get you fired for being so snotty.”

No way did anybody promise her the paper before it’s even loaded on trucks. Nobody would believe I’m snotty to a customer, either. But such is the power of a grownup, even talking crazy and mean for no reason, that I feel bad and say I’ll ask if anything can be done.

“Wait,” DL says. “Don’t you want your money? Sheesh!”

So much for soaking wet Saturday collections. So-so payment-wise, and everybody with one exception is nice enough. But nobody—not one—gives me strokes for being the great paperboy I knock myself to be.

State of Overwhelm

I catch a break between waves of rain and ride my route with thoughts from the morning going around and around in my head. I don't want to talk about it at dinner. And I hope that all-knowing, all-seeing you-know-who does not notice me not wanting to talk.

Lots of luck with that. It's Saturday and my sisters have gone out on dates. It's just the three of us for dinner.

He turns to me. "How'd those collection calls go, Steve?"

Two ways to proceed: I can see if I'll get away with "Fine"—or I tell all.

After I tell, Dad says, "Welcome to the world of customer feedback and suggestions!"

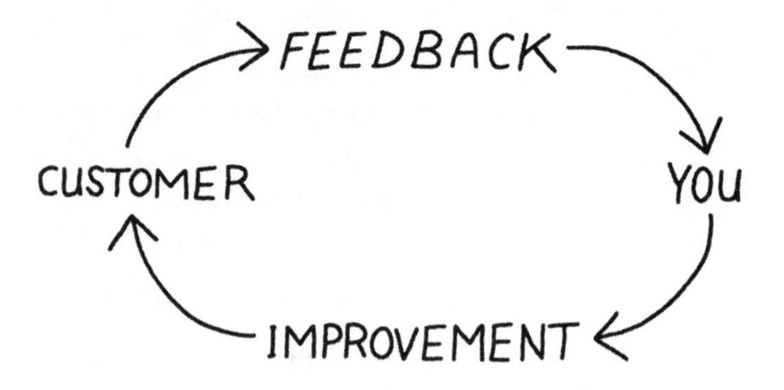

He wants to know if I asked for any of the input and goes on, "Ah, unsolicited feedback! Asked for or not, even if you don't like hearing it, this is how you find out how to improve your service."

"By giving that lady her paper when it isn't printed, and I'm still in school?"

"We'll get back to that one. Why do the others bother you, as they obviously do?"

"If I have to do special stuff for everybody who asks . . ."

"I am so glad you can help Pete Hutchinson. He's lucky he survived that accident. And nobody knows if he'll be able to walk."

"But if everybody asks . . ."

"Is everybody home from the hospital in a wheelchair?"

"No, but I think Legendary Lowell was talking about putting papers behind everybody's screen doors when it rains, not just his."

"You know, you may be right about that."

Un-Looping Feedback

"The guys were all glad to have Lowell in the platoon."

"Because he's so funny?"

"That, yes. And he was always working an angle. Soldiers do, but mostly for themselves. Lowell knew how to work the sergeant and the officers for general benefit. And we got perks and cushy jobs like nobody's business."

Dad chuckles at some memory, then says, "You might want to consider his suggestion about that extra bit of service for customers when it rains. It may have some real merit."

"Dad, that's extra time at seventy houses!"

“You were saying you’ve cut your route time in half, so there’s your extra. It doesn’t rain all that often in Salt Lake, anyway. And consider the benefits.”

“For who? Only one person asked.”

“For whom, with an ‘m.’ One asked; they will all appreciate it. Sometimes feedback leads to customized service, like for the Hutchinsons. That’s an exception. Other times you get a suggestion that’s good for everybody, including your business, and you make it a rule for one and all.”

“I think I get it.”

“Here’s a chance to do what we were talking about, to do more than right by your customers when nothing’s wrong, and maybe they go from satisfied to loyal.”

“Maybe you’re right, Dad.”

Dad comes to a twist in the trail and says, “Funny word, feedback. That’s what you call it when somebody turns on a microphone and gets that horrible screech.”

“Yeah, like the principal at assemblies. Everybody laughs!”

“It happens because the mike picks up sound from the speakers, which feeds back into the mike and comes out of the speakers, louder and screechier, until somebody makes adjustments. You need to work your own controls when you get feedback, Steve.”

“What do you mean?”

"You make adjustments based on customers' input, and get clear and pleasant sound because your people are happier with their service."

"What about feedback that's evil and insane, like the Dragon Lady yelling about getting her paper before it's even printed?"

"Unreasonable might be a better way to put it. But even she deserves a respectful listen and response."

"I never want to go back there!"

"You said she's at work when you deliver. Drop off a respectful note, saying you inquired about her request. And if her needs can't be met, she and her business will be missed."

"Wait, when did I inquire?"

"You just did, and I answered. Remember, Steve, when a customer speaks you listen, carefully consider what you hear, and be ready to act on what they tell you. Feedback. Listen. Respond. That's how a Where People Mean Everything business acts."

"Speaking of input to act on: Jan, what do you say we go out with Steve to take in a movie. Popcorn during the show and ice cream afterward!"

Get Pedaling

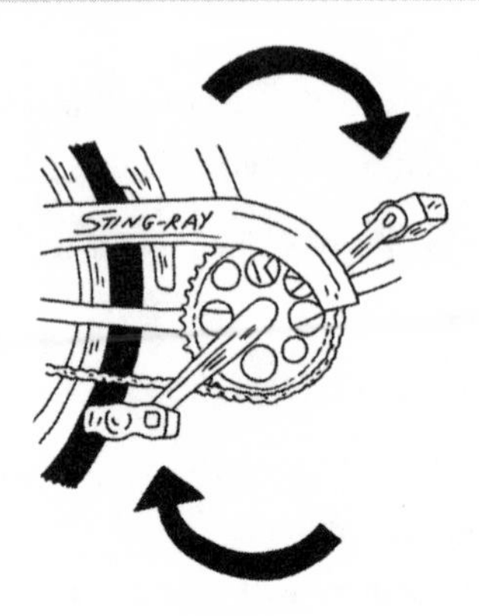

The Challenge

Get, and get the most out of, valuable feedback from your clientele.

Ask for feedback on a regular basis and track responses. Have protocols in place for recording and handling input you don't ask for, too. Most important, do something with responses. And always let customers know they are listened-to and appreciated for their feedback.

Much More than Scores

Feedback that counts most in a Where People Mean Everything business comes from live encounters between your team and people. And it's about the personal side of your service, i.e., emotions.

No disrespect to systems that get feedback data and crunch it with cutting-edge computer analysis. This stuff is brilliant and getting more so all the time. What you get, though, are brilliant scores.

You need more.

Get more by going past statistics and scores to what your clients reveal in direct communication.

What You Get

It's worth the effort, because it's gold.

Understand people's feelings about what you do and how you do it—high, low, good here, bad there—and you have information that leads to results-producing action. When asked correctly, people tell you what you need to do more of or change to do better by them. And that means doing better in your business.

Plan, Create a System

Make asking for feedback at specific points of engagement a task for which team members are accountable. It is best to do it at the end of the service experience. In a health care environment this could be at the desk where the patients check out and make follow-up appointments, in a restaurant when the waitstaff bring the receipt and credit card slip, or at the end of a customer service phone call.

You don't have to do it with every customer, but specify a number of daily asks. Make it a for-real task.

Establish protocols and accountability for sharing the day's responses, so feedback goes up to supervision and management and around the team to those who will most benefit. Good news? Share it with the team and make those responsible feel proud and happy. The team will know more of the same quality of work is called for.

On the negative side, it's vital to find out where improvements need to be made. These may tie into individual performance or be procedural, in a system that needs fixing.

Quick, Easy

Keep it conversational, with a feeling of sincere person-to-person interest.

Start with "How was your experience today?" or equivalent words that feel natural. Don't let "Fine" stop the conversation; follow up with a more open-ended question. "We love hearing that. If you don't mind my asking, what was your favorite part?"

Come back with shared enthusiasm, like, "I'll be sure to pass that on. Your comfort is really important to all of us," or "Ooh, that's one of my favorites, too. I'll be sure and tell Chef Maria."

If it's a "Fine," that seems more polite than positive, go for a little more, like "Hmm, what would it take to get you up to 'Fabulous!' next time you come in?"

Negative input gets a more serious version of the same engagement and interest. Take immediate action to correct the situation, if possible. Or give assurance the feedback will be passed on to someone in a position to do something about it. Then follow up.

No matter the kind of input, a great big "Thanks!" is in order because the customer just gave you and the team something of value.

Listen, Look For

Emotion behind and between the words. Problems need to be fixed on the emotional level as well as at the service level.

Think back to customer feedback driven by feelings in this chapter:

- Asking for the paper in the mail slot, Mrs. Hutchinson really wants a little less upset and pain in the aftermath of her husband's traumatic injury. If he can get the paper on his own while she's at work, he has an enjoyable distraction. And she has less to worry about.
- Legendary Lowell's suggestion to put papers inside doors on wet days is all about avoidable annoyance—his and everybody else's, too. Nobody wants to get rained-on to get the paper.
- Who knows what lurks in the heart of Dragon Lady and what, if anything, I could do to make it better? But a customer making irrational demands, disgruntled for

disgruntlement's sake, is still a customer. She, too, deserves due consideration and a respectful response, which she gets.

Unsolicited Feedback and Feedback Culture

All three of the above examples are unsolicited feedback. The major difference, versus feedback you ask for, is lack of predictability and control. You don't know when you're going to get it, and who on the service team will be there.

Train the whole team to communicate with customers, understand their praise or specific criticism, and have well-designed protocols to pass on the specifics to the right people.

Cultivate a 360-degree Feedback Culture so the whole team values outside input and knows what to do with it.

Exceptions, Rules, Get "No" Out of the Head

In this chapter, Legendary Lowell's suggestion, if adopted, is a new route-wide rule affecting everybody. Mrs. Hutchinson asks for an exception, affecting only deliveries to her house. Both times the decision comes down to a simple question: Do or don't? And a couple follow-ups: Is this a reasonable, doable one-off that will engender individual loyalty and satisfaction? Or, is this a system-wide improvement that can positively impact everyone's loyalty and satisfaction?

Most Important Feedback

Make a special effort to reach out to people after a fail and your attempts at a Great Recovery. Ask them, "How are you now?" and if everything has been resolved to their satisfaction.

Closing the Circle

Customers need to know and feel that they are listened to, and that their feedback is noticed and duly considered. Always be appreciative of feedback—positive or negative—in person, online, or on any platform. Let people know it will be duly considered.

Draw the line at abuse, which nobody needs to take. And don't go to the dark side yourself.

So...

What is your Feedback Culture?

No. 00001
FIRST NATIONAL BANK
SALT LAKE CITY, UTAH
DATE 4/1/78
$??!!
PAY TO THE ORDER OF NEWS Co LTD
THE EXACT CORRECT AMOUNT ONLY DOLLARS
Steven J Anderson
MEMO papers
0003865412345-4

Chapter 7

Where the Bucks Stop

CFO Mom

The way Mom handles family finances and keeps the books, dollars and cents are terrified not to add up and balance out. I would not be surprised if now, more than forty years later, we could find the records she enters working at the dining room table this particular afternoon.

This is right before I go see Mrs. Hanson, my route supervisor, for our monthly accounting. Before I leave, I want to spread out my paper route stuff and make it more presentable because last time I got sort of a "hmmph." And Mrs. Hanson had to show me, once again, how to organize and work through my numbers to reconcile with hers. "Typical of new kids," she said. This time I want to nail it.

"Let's see what you have, Steve," Mom says and motions for me to sit down by her.

After the half-frown and squeeze of her mouth, my collections sheet should crumple up and throw itself out. “You can do better than this,” is the message to me, silent but loud and clear. She has me get another sheet off the pad and hands me a pencil to recopy the entries. Then she slides over her business-y little adding machine that prints on cool paper off a roll. I punch in numbers, rip off the skinny printout, staple it to the collections sheet, and go straight to preteen business nerd heaven!

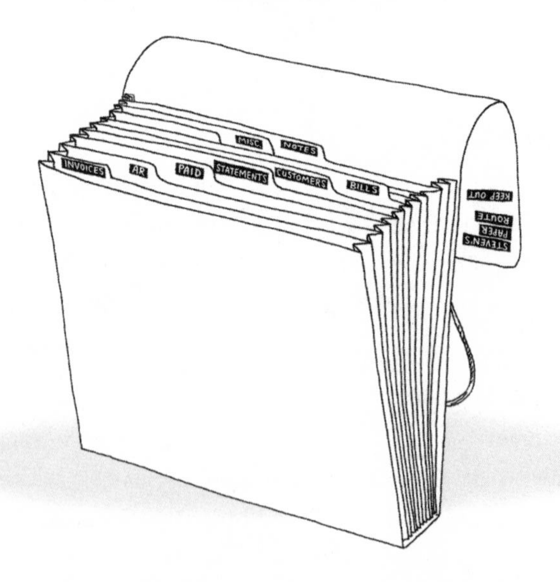

In no time everything’s sorted by category and date, paper-clipped and with adding machine tallies. The stuff goes in a good-as-new accordion file with pouches neatly re-labeled. One contains a list of customers who haven’t paid yet, with machine totaling, under the initials AR that Mom says stand for Accounts

Receivable. Her top-of-the-bifocals look at me says this is stuff I should take more seriously.

"Thanks, Mom!" and I am on the Sting-Ray.

Some guys I know playing catch and running bases look like they're having fun, but I would not switch places. How many kids in Salt Lake are on the way to a business meeting with paperwork in an accordion file? Who will write out an actual check at said meeting? And even have a clue what AR means?

None, that's how many—except for me, CEO and president of my paper route, and I am about to knock Mrs. Hanson right off her dining chair!

The Velvet Brick Wall

Mrs. Hanson is a pleasant person of an age I can't even guess. Everybody's old when you're twelve, right? Her dining room table is smaller than ours, presumably because the family is smaller. And, look at this, today I see she has exactly the same kind of adding machine as Mom.

Super-neatness does make an impression. Mrs. Hanson says, "Tell whoever showed you how to put things together like this—your mother, I'm going to guess—that this is professional work."

She tells about running into Mrs. Somebody at Smith's Food King and hearing about how friendly and polite I am. And how I put the papers inside the screen door on the last couple rainy afternoons.

“That’s an original move, Steve,” Mrs. Hanson says. “I am impressed.”

You and me both. Putting People Mean Everything points on the board! And rockin’ positive word of mouth!

I get some “Nice job” nods reconciling my stuff and hers, with an adjustment in my favor from deliveries not made while people were away.

The AR list prompts a question: “Did you have this many last month?”

I can’t answer. She says, “I don’t think so. We’ll know in dollars and cents in a minute, when you write me the check.”

She means a check for what I owe the company for papers delivered to customers. She puts a number on paper and says, “Make the check out in this amount.”

An unwritten, unspoken dollar figure is where I have skin in the game. That’s the amount I collect over and above the amount about to be paid by check. Talking about the most beautiful number of all—my profit!

The ballpark figure I do in my head hurts.

“Are you sure this is right?”

“Well, we just worked it out together.”

She’s right; we did. But is she really right to make me pay for every single one of this month’s no-pays?

Like, say, the family on top of the AR list. Mrs. O'Malley actually called from Oregon about forgetting to pay before they left town because her dad suddenly got sick. She mailed the check from Portland.

"You'll probably have it tomorrow," Mrs. Hanson says.

Okay then. She'll let me off the hook on this one.

Or not. She points to the same number and says, "This is how much you owe."

Mrs. Hanson completely understands my problems running down Mr. and/or Mrs. Jameson, who paid in person on previous collection days, no problem, but were not home last Saturday.

"Write the check for that much."

She understands that Mr. Gelson, another very reliable customer, forgot to put a stamp on the payment envelope so the mailman left it instead of taking it to be sent, and Mrs. Gelson who was out shopping when I came to collect had it, along with the checkbook, in her pocketbook.

"You need to write the check for this amount."

She listens when I tell about a couple other gold-plate customers who have not paid yet. She does not disagree that they will come through. She gets how much work it is to do collections on top of my deliveries and seems to feel my frustration.

But, but, but… "This is how much you owe, Steve."

She's like a brick wall covered in velvet—nice but immoveable.

I write the check, get on my bike, and ride.

"It's not fair!"

I'm not sure, but I sincerely hope I scream it only in my head and not out loud on the ride home. Why should I have to pay when customers don't? They get their newspapers. I do the work, plus the work of chasing around no-pays that I still have to pay for. Negative pay is even more unfair than no pay. The company gets money no matter what. And what I get, no matter what, is absolutely not fair!

Flirty Socrates

After dinner prayer and the usual minutes of quiet power eating, Dad speaks up.

"You know, we had our monthly financial meeting today. And, not for the first time, it came to me that our accounting team could learn a few lessons from your mother. Nothing slips by her. Not only that, she's beautiful and absolutely brilliant at whatever she turns her hand to."

"Oh, Arthur"—her stock response to him getting carried away.

Flirty parents make a nice distraction from no-pays and pathetic profits.

Dad goes on, "Steve, I understand you, too, had a lesson in keeping books and accounting."

"It was great. Thanks, Mom."

"Your mother told me about the AR."

Of course she did. Can't they just argue, like other people's parents?

"That's a common source of problems, especially starting out. Let things slip, and you find out you're not doing as well as you thought down on the bottom line. Your profit line. And you feel blindsided."

"That's exactly how I feel."

"Don't be too hard on yourself."

"Why would I be? Why not be hard on the people who get papers but don't pay, and I have to because they don't?"

"Why not, indeed . . ."

"Or the company that puts me in the middle?"

"That too, yes," Dad muses.

"And why won't Mrs. Hanson cut me any slack, even a little, for customers she says she knows are going to pay?"

"They bear none of the blame, which falls squarely on you—as well as the financial responsibility and work you may never get paid for. Can this be fair?"

"Come on, Dad. What do you think?"

Long pause. Dad, like Socrates, can only say what he truly thinks.

Accountability and Pudding

"Steve, I think it is absolutely fair. And I want you to think that, too."

"What?"

"You know what most people really mean when they say, 'It's not fair?'"

"Probably that it's not fair."

"Most times it's more like, 'I don't like it. Even though I knew what I signed on for, it's harder than I thought, and I don't like it!'"

"You're saying that's me?"

"I'm saying you can make it fair, and learn to like it and ultimately love it, by taking full personal responsibility for results, all results, in your business. By so doing, you will serve your people the right way, like they truly are everything."

"People who don't pay are everything?"

"Whose problem is it if they don't pay? And whose responsibility is it to find them and persuade them to, before it's too late and you get hit where it hurts in front of your route supervisor? Who's accountable to her and the company?"

"Me, I guess."

"No guessing about it!"

Compared to some of the other Q&As at dinner, this one's pretty straight and quick. From now on, I treat ARs as to-dos, important ones, to be checked off as done before it's time to see Mrs. Hanson. I will never, ever try to get her to cut me slack again. Coming up short is nobody's problem but mine. I'll attack it on all sides, including reminder notes for no-pays and known slow-pays after the payment envelopes go out. I'll get out and do the big round of in-person collections earlier. I'll push doorbells and catch the last no-pays when I'm out on the route.

"Diligence pays, Steve, in this and everything else. And the little stuff isn't little. Get face to face, and it's only the rare customer who won't do what's right. On the other hand, it doesn't take many un-paid collections to hurt. As you discovered!"

Oh no, he's looking into the Dad Zone. What now?

"You know, Son, your father owes you an apology. A bit ago, I said don't be hard on yourself."

"I think you said *too hard* on myself."

"*Almost* too hard is good, though. In business, you have to be hard on yourself. That's the only way to make things easier. And to enjoy life's hard-earned rewards. As we are about to."

Dad turns to Mom. "Janice, my lily, my Rose of Sharon…"

"Stop, we'll lose our appetites," Mom says.

"Heart of my heart, what's for dessert?"

"Banana pudding with vanilla wafers."

"A personal favorite. I will personally serve it. Steve will help."

Get Pedaling

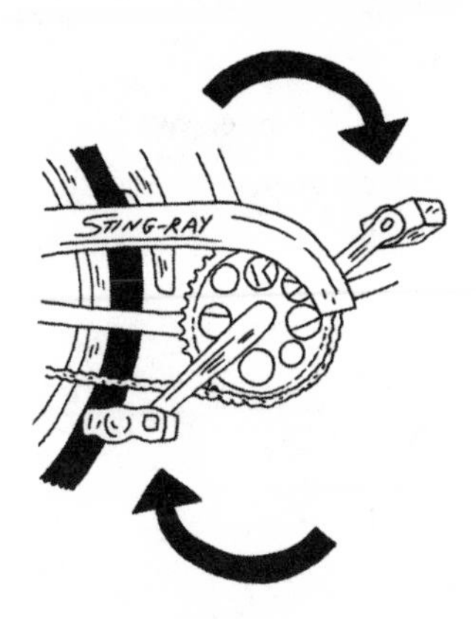

The Challenge

Get the *wah wah waah* from the aggrieved, put-upon inner-twelve-year-old out of your head. Face and own all that is yours. Deliver results for which you are responsible and accountable. Like it or not—or even hate some of it—your stuff is yours. Don't be surprised if you do like some of it, when you quit going *wah wah waah*.

This Get Pedaling is different because you're doing some, maybe most, of the actual writing.

Do you think it's unfair, being told to write when you thought you were just reading?

Tough. Just do it. You'll achieve more, get better results, and feel better about it.

On-Paper Scapegoat

The scapegoat in the Old Testament was an actual goat. The chief priest of the ancient Hebrews symbolically loaded everybody's sins on a goat. It was driven into the wilderness where it met a lonely, horrible end.

Really unfair to the goat. But the ancient Hebrews felt much better and got on with their lives.

You get a goat written on paper, or digitally, with a similar intended effect. You get rid of stuff you really don't want.

Exercise #1: Blamegoats

List go-to people and things you blame for your problems. Stuff like…

- Jeannine not doing her job
- Liam not knowing how to do his
- System that rewards do-nothings and incompetents
- Crazy customers
- Sabotage from other work teams
- Boss who is… (a) incompetent, (b) mean, (c) threatened because you're better/smarter/younger
- Family that holds you back

- Boyfriend/girlfriend who doesn't understand and provide support
- Equipment that's old, bad, wrong for the job
- The economy
- Horrible bus line making you late

Go crazy. Leave no blame unturned. Don't stop until you have at least 21 blames you've actually used to make excuses for yourself.

#2 Complaingoat

Next comes unfair circumstances and treatment, especially where you bear burdens that should not, no way no how, be yours. Unfairness is everywhere in life. For present purposes, stick close to your role in your service business.

If it helps, think of twelve-year-old-me in a snit about the unfair system wherein I lose pay for work I do when people don't pay me. And how Mrs. Hanson, really unfairly, refuses to cut me slack.

Proceed in the same spirit, like…

- It's unfair that I, who make and plate $40 main dishes in a place featured in *Bon Appetit* magazine, have to help clean and take out garbage at closing.
- I don't get anywhere near fair (pick one) pay/recognition/ appreciation for the brilliant work I do.

- I did all this fantastic work and nobody used it or said "Boo."
- So much time is tied up in dumb routine that a trained sheepdog could do on top of my real super-demanding job.
- I leave late and get home so exhausted.

Don't stop 'til you run out of your go-to complaints.

#3 Call BS on Yourself

Time to get real.

Go through the lists and cross out stuff that is self-serving, self-pitying nonsense. It helps to pretend somebody else is saying/feeling the same things in similar situations. If it sounds even a little *wah wah waah*, cross it out.

Even where there's something nobody in their right mind would like, and they might legitimately feel dumped on, get real about that, too. Join the human race living in this world of work.

It is what it is. And it's yours.

It's okay and you're okay if you don't like some of it. You'll dislike it more if you complain about it and don't do it well.

#4 All Yours

Get real about your must-dos—job responsibilities, specific tasks, and results for which you are accountable. You and nobody else.

Big stuff that gets you ahead in the world and little stuff you wish would go away.

Star tasks and accountabilities you especially don't like.

Double-star tasks where results are so-so or worse because you let them slide.

#5 Plan

This is a rudimentary from-scratch start on a Grand Plan.

Load the *wah wah waah* on the goat and get rid of it. If it comes back, chase it away again.

Make a plan to get more and better results out of each must-do in the preceding list.

Put the juice not on the big stuff, but on little stuff you don't like and really want to let slide.

Remember that in the grand scheme of things, messing up on little stuff gets in the way of big stuff and can hold you back.

So don't.

Own it all.

So…

What's your plan to quit with the *wah wah waah* and do what needs doing, big stuff and small? No blame. No complain.

Chapter 8

Snow Day

Strange Awakening

Dad stands in my bedroom, which is so dark it takes an effort to make out details like his monster buckle-up rubber galoshes. Odd with the Mr. Mac suit, starched shirt, and tie. He holds both his briefcase and a snow shovel.

"Rise and shine, Steve! Your services are required. Wait 'til you see how it's coming down!"

Okay, this is not a dream. My around-home responsibilities include driveway and sidewalk snow removal. At last night's dinner, Dad said we might see some snow.

No big deal, not in our part of the world. And until it's upon us, even forecasters are clueless about the freakish, historic, multiple-record-breaker late spring snowstorm.

Who doesn't love a weather apocalypse that's mostly harmless? Dad may be unique in also using it in a short pre-dawn seminar. While I have cocoa in the kitchen, he talks about low-probability events that still must be prepared for. Unusual is usual. Always, always expect the best and plan for the worst.

"Why? Because it can happen. And when, not if, it does, you must be prepared to do business as usual and serve your clientele. W-I-T. Whatever It Takes. That's one worth remembering."

"Oh, Arthur," says Mom. "There's no amount of preparation for driving on streets that the mayor just declared on the radio that you should not drive on. Since it's past season, there's no snow removal equipment ready. We already have eighteen inches on the ground!"

"I tell the team we do Whatever It Takes to serve our clients. Leaders lead, Jan."

"Of course. And they also drive all over to pick up employees too sensible to take their own cars."

"That's the team for today's publicity rollout in Las Vegas. Southern Nevada does not care about Utah's snow!"

Never Is Now

A non-Anderson would not know they just heard an argument. Margaret, Heidi, and I share a look. Wow—Mom does not want Dad driving to work.

Mom has the sisters laying out candles, flashlights and extra batteries from her power outage supplies, just in case. She also directs a sandwich assembly line and, of course, has her cookie jar locked and loaded. Weather emergencies, like all agents of chaos, don't stand a chance against Mom.

She answers the kitchen phone, hangs up and says, "Wendy Sebring says the city schools have just declared a Snow Day."

"That never happens!"

More than one of us says it. Everybody thinks it. It's a point of pride—no, it's who we are—to not call off school like other wimpy cities.

Dad lights up and declares, "Well, never is now, people. Point proven!"

Out in the garage, Dad puts a shovel and bag of sand in the Chrysler's trunk and then turns and places his hands on my shoulders.

"When a newsworthy event happens, what do people want?"

"A lot of things?"

"The want that matters in your business is this: People want the news. And your paper will go to print today to provide it. Whose people are some of the paper's people?"

"Mine."

"Steve, even if the snow keeps coming all day and they give you an out, like a Paperboy Snow Day, forget it. Do your best to take care of your people. Figure it out. Be ready. W-I-T! What does that stand for?"

"Whatever It Takes!"

I will never forget Dad's sendoff. All of us stand by the car in snow that's a wonder to behold. The driveway I just shoveled bare is already white.

"You really won't see reason?" Mom knows the answer. She actually means, *Be careful. I love you. You are brave but foolish and please don't wreck our beautiful new car.*

Mom says to the girls, "Put the box with lunches and thermoses on the back seat." Then to Dad, smiling, "Fearless Leader is now prepared to feed his people, too."

Dad sits, wordless. Then he rolls up the driver's side window and starts down the drive. The car does fine until it hits the unplowed and untracked street. Spinning tires whine as the car fishtails and slowly rolls away. The Chrysler pushes snow like one of the plows that's not coming. Neighbors out to shovel, or just yack with others, stand and watch.

A 1978 Chrysler New Yorker is a magnificent specimen of great big Detroit iron. One day people will consider this model a collectible classic, just like my purple 1960s Schwinn Sting-Ray.

They're both worse than useless on snow.

Do-Something Day

Snow Day means Do-Nothing Day, unless you live in a house where idleness is against the law.

Out in the garage, I set up for wet-day delivery of my newspapers, plastic bags and rubber bands out and ready. I need to save time because slogging through knee-deep snow to seventy houses will take forever. After that I take time to adjust, lube, clean, and polish my bike, which has had lots of messy riding and not enough love. I have it upside down, adjusting the coaster brake, when I hear Mom's voice.

"Please don't tell me you intend to ride that thing. One Anderson on wheels today is more than I can bear."

"No Mom, just fixing."

"You need to come in and call Mrs. Hanson. And when you're off the phone, you can shovel again, the way the snow's piling up."

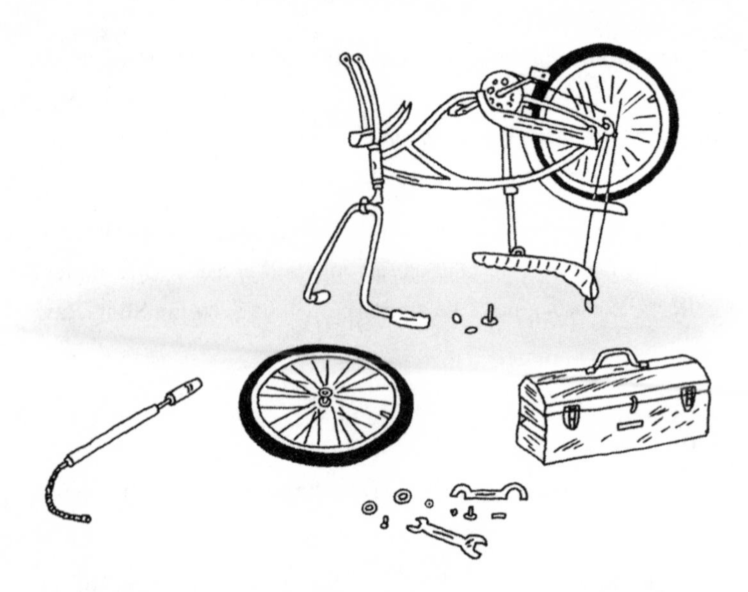

A man serves many supervisors, right? The one on the phone says she'll call again with updates on today's drop-offs. The company's still not sure when trucks will go out and if side streets like ours will even be drivable.

"Standing by for further instructions!"

Yeah, I love saying this, and the whole emergency vibe. Early afternoon brings major bulletins. I have to be ready for an earlier drop-off that won't be at the house. They have designated spots out on major streets that are reachable.

Before she hangs up, Mrs. Hanson says that the company understands that some routes may not get delivered tonight. Impossible is, well, impossible. It can't be helped.

Thanks, Mrs. H., but no thanks. Steve does not do Snow Days.

But pulling this off will be tough. W-I-T for sure, but I'm not sure what's the Whatever it will take.

While I have a pick-me-up cookie and milk, Mom looks at Heidi, who gives me some kind of big-sister eyes.

"If you want some help, Steve," Mom says.

"Why would I need help?"

"Well, Margaret's busy on a research paper, but Heidi has caught up on all her schoolwork."

"I told you he wouldn't be interested," Heidi says.

"Let your brother speak."

What choice do I have when people have already decided on my behalf? And, you know, help could really help.

I get the snow sled down for hauling newspapers, Heidi dresses for the weather, and Mom says, "You two have fun!"

"Of course. My friends will be green with envy," Heidi says.

Then, two doors from home, we start having fun. Just like kids dragging a sled. She rides a bit, then I do, we say "Hi" to strangers and people we know, then load the papers and come back home. Laughing all the way, just like in "Jingle Bells," which we actually sing. By then Heidi wants to do part of my route, as I have been dying to ask her to.

"Let me think about it," I say, and she says she'll be an old lady before I'm capable of rational thought.

Thank you, Sister!

Back home, we go into the kitchen for a quick warmup, and Margaret comes in and says, "Whatever you two are up to, count me in. I claim Bigger Sister rights."

She says that if Heidi helps deliver papers, she will, too. Mom gives me a shrug of surprise and "Why not?" and then gets managerial. "We need to sit down right now and map out how to do this. Preparation and planning!"

We go to the dining room table and literally map out a plan using my route lists and diagrams sketched out by Margaret.

"That," declares Mom, "was fourteen minutes well spent. Better get going, time's a-wastin'. Dinner will be buffet style in the kitchen whenever you get back. Your father says don't wait for him. He'll be late without the car."

Uh-oh. Concern all around.

"He made a very sensible decision to leave it in the building garage. The Chrysler's fine."

Right, Right, Right Meets W-I-T

Even when two of them are new to this, three people prepping and packing papers are faster than one. Then I pull the sled, and Margaret and Heidi carry bags that are much lighter than the full load I hang on my bike. The sisters each work off a name-and-address list, with a few houses starred where we decide it's a good idea to knock and see that the people are okay.

Today, of all days, I get a bye on Right, Right, Right, even from Mrs. Hanson. Non-delivery would cost me zero customer satisfaction points. Nobody on the route reasonably expects a paper, much less a paper behind the screen door. But that is exactly what they get, before six o'clock. Yay us, Steve and Team W-I-T!

No problem that we get home at straight-up six, starving hungry, because tonight we can eat right away in the kitchen. We tear into Mom's sloppy joes, salad, and potato chips. Food-wise, Snow Day is just like the Fourth of July.

"Well, how was it?" Mom asks.

"So much fun. I wish I'd had a paper route when I was twelve," Margaret says.

"I see why Steve likes it," says Heidi.

"Well, the people liked it. The nicest calls came in, not one complaint."

When dessert would be in order, Mom says, "We will sit down and have chocolate cake and ice cream after your father gets home."

That happens more than an hour after he usually bounds in, and he is not capable of bounding.

"Look what the cat dragged in," Mom says.

"No cat, I'm dragging myself." He explains that there's pretty much nothing moving, but a county truck driver took pity and gave him a lift part of the way.

"After that, I broke trail."

"And in your best suit and new overcoat. How did things go down in Las Vegas?"

"The client now wants to work with us in other markets."

"Well done, Arthur."

He has nothing more to say on that or any other subject.

Socrates Declares a Snow Day!

Dad just eats and smiles while Margaret and Heidi get going about their adventures on my paper route. One says she had a big laugh with the lady whose window I smashed, and she plans to drop in now and again on old Mrs. Simpson and Mrs. Taylor, who are so sweet. The other says it's so cool to peek in and see people's furniture and pictures and that Mrs. Dunbar the Dragon Lady came to the door and said thanks for the newspaper with smoke blowing out her nose. Legendary Lowell had her rolling in the snow laughing.

Mom chimes in with the complimentary calls and one she hadn't mentioned from Mrs. Hanson, who was amazed at the on-time delivery. She also told Mom I am not allowed to delegate delivery of papers without prior notification of my route supervisor. "However, anything goes today. Mrs. Hanson said she will pass on the story of heroic home delivery to the City Desk at the paper. Congratulations!"

Dad locks eyes with me, winks, and does something funny: He says, slowly, "Right—Right—Right." And with each word he points to Margaret, Heidi, and me.

And then he says, "Whatever—It—Takes." And points to us in reverse order.

He blinks away wetness in his eyes that must be left over from fighting the storm winds and from being so tired.

"I need to go take a long, hot shower," he says, "but not 'til after our cake and ice cream!"

Get Pedaling

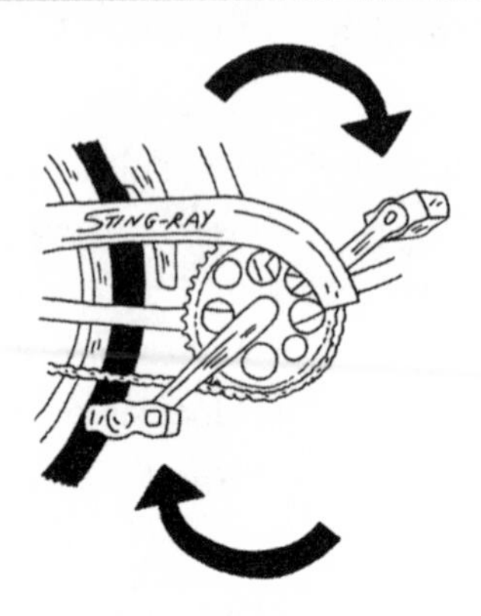

The Challenge

Revise your attitude and thinking and do Whatever It Takes to deliver on your Service Promise and Service Standard. Perceive unexpected, seemingly unsurmountable obstacles in a positive way—"Oh boy!" not "Oh no!"—and find ways over and around whatever suddenly, expectedly stands in the way of you and your team.

Inspire team members and become a legend to customers by doing W-I-T, Whatever It Takes.

Inside Job

Ask yourself, and answer honestly, what you are willing and not willing to do to make sure your promises to customers are kept.

When obstacles mount and seem to stand in the way of regular, smooth operation, what's your reflexive response?

Are you excited at being called on to go above and beyond, to find original solutions on the spot?

Do you see new opportunity to take your service to the level of legend, and earn new customer loyalty?

Or…

Do you tend to do what you're required to do and let that suffice? Then feel good that you made a reasonable effort—reasonable meaning within the bounds of the expectations of your customers and your team?

Is that enough? Should it be?

You choose.

And you make the choice by choosing your attitude in the face of obstacles.

W-I-T Culture

Your team makes its choice, too. Having looked within yourself, look at those you work with.

Organizations are all over on W-I-T culture. If yours is policy-driven, boundaries both real and perceived will be on everybody's mind. This sort of culture can be riddled with constraints that aren't really there, people stuck in imaginary boxes. Whatever It

Takes thinking and doing, by nature out-of-the-box, has a tough time where rigid rules rule.

On the other hand, your organization may embrace W-I-T, encouraging its people to look for ways to go above and beyond, and recognizing them when they do.

Either way, know and get straight with your culture.

And Talk about It

Do what you did in your own head, out loud and with others. Get understanding and consensus about where the team is in its willingness to think fast and take action when it gets tough to serve customers in the usual manner. Spell out who's authorized to do what to do right by customers, and where the limits are.

You don't know exactly what obstacles will arise, or what solutions apply. By definition, it will be unusual, beyond expectation, possibly beyond imagining until it happens.

Is your team ready?

W-I-T in Action

This example is a relatively small-scale response, involving service to one person. Most teams would not even think to respond in this manner.

A patient on her way to a dental appointment stops to get coffee. Then her car won't start. She phones with profuse apologies that she can't make it.

Except she can, and does, make it right on time. And she gets her scheduled care from the dentist.

How? The team member who took her call put her on hold, ordered pickup from a rideshare service, then came back on the line and told the patient to sit tight. Help was on the way.

More Is More than Worth It

In any other office, the team member taking the call would say, "So sorry you're having problems. Give us a call when you're ready to reschedule." And they'd feel good about the way they handled it.

But the W-I-T solution has benefits all around. For the dental practice, it saves many more times what it costs in terms of lost chair time and juggling the schedule to re-book, and—above all—it provides Right, Right, Right service to somebody in need of dental care. All it takes is a step out of the box, and everything proceeds smoothly for everybody.

Stuff of Legend

Did the patient expect this? Of course not.

Better believe she'll never forget it, and she will tell the world about it, too—"You're not going to believe what the dental office did for me this morning."

Legends are what you get when you step out of the box for the people you serve. And in many cases, like this one, there's a direct bottom-line benefit for you, too. Delivering on promises is always good business.

Know Your Limits

Absolute limits involve safety and respecting the law.

Organizational policies and rules may come in, too.

And there's common sense.

If, say, your patient was held up by a maintenance problem on her flight back home, you would not charter a jet to go get her. Or a helicopter or boat.

Mindset and Perception

W-I-T is like augmented reality. In the mind's eye, you see the work-arounds that get you over, around, or past the obstacle entirely.

And Fun

Take a pass on W-I-T, and you miss out on more than business. You miss out on a lot of fun, too, to be shared with the whole team and, of course, the client. It's great to amaze yourself and others by what you can do in a pinch.

And it's great for the clients to be amazed.

Just figuring things out, thinking through a novel solution to the unexpected, is its own kind of challenge and entertainment.

Just as I needed my sisters on my side to deliver the papers on our famous Snow Day, your W-I-T win will probably involve a team effort. Shared excitement is more exciting, and the fans—i.e., clientele—cheer you on and remember the extraordinary effort.

So…

What is your Whatever It Takes attitude?

Chapter 9

Doing Good

Nana's Hands and Dad's Dessert

There's more to my Dad's thing for dessert than a sweet tooth bigger than any of his kids have. More than all of us put together, actually. Treats at dinner's end take him to a happy place where he has gone since boyhood. And it honors his mother's heroics to do for Dad and his two brothers.

Dad grew up seeing Whatever It Takes in action. Mildred Anderson, Nana to her fifteen grandkids, raised her boys on her own as a young widow in the worst of the Great Depression. Nana lost her husband unexpectedly when Dad was just nine years old. She turned her hands to whatever work she could do and still look after her boys. For a time she hand-made forty loaves of bread a day, baked them in the oven of a coal-fired stove, and sent her boys out to sell the bread. No matter how lean things got, she scraped together ingredients to make dessert for her sons.

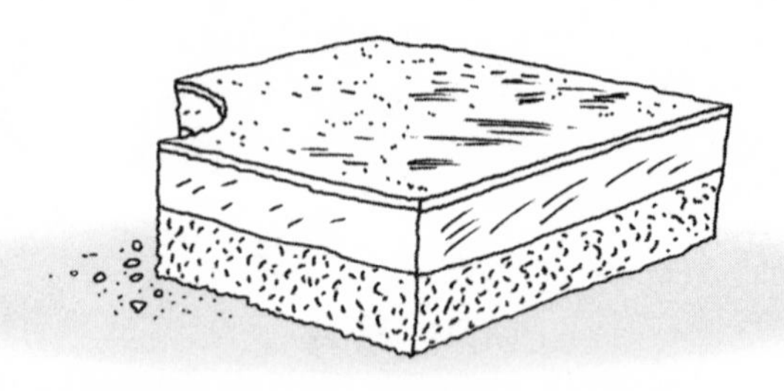

With her own two hands, Nana made bad times better every single day. As Dad says, "I never felt we were poor when we had dessert."

By the time I'm twelve, Nana's hands are crabbed and knotted with arthritis, and they tremble from Parkinson's Disease. It takes time and major effort to close a Zip-loc bag. She has to work to pour me a glass of milk. She picks it up two-handed because her fingers won't bend to hold it. Then it's a journey to the table in her little kitchen where we love to sit and visit. This we get to do on a weekly basis in the warm, green months of the year.

We Andersons are all pleased to lend our hands to Nana. I naturally grew into sole responsibility for mowing, weeding the flower beds, and what-all in her yard.

The instant the weather stops making jerky moves, snow one day and hot the next, grass has explosive growth and weeds try to outdo the lawn and other legit plants. And here I go on a Saturday morning, making the ten-block haul to Nana's place on the Sting-Ray.

I've got new hand tools and special fertilizer and seeds in my newspaper bags. Later, Dad will drop off flats of already-blooming bedding plants and a couple bags of wood-chip mulch. He'll do it on the hush-hush, so Nana won't see until the flowers are planted.

This stuff will be amazing around Nana's cute little cottage!

No, this is not business related. It's true that I did some lawnmowing, raking, and basic yard work for other people last summer and expect to keep working for them this upcoming season. The money isn't bad. True, too, that I plan to offer more complete landscaping services and expand my clientele, beginning with my loyal newspaper customers. But this is not some kind of showplace display for marketing purposes. It isn't for my pleasure, either.

It's a big surprise for Nana.

Please Yourself

"What's going on? Who's here? Whose bicycle is that?"

She fakes the old-person confusion for humorous effect. Nana sticks her head out the door and, as we all do, I wonder at her mane of thick, naturally curly, snow-white hair.

"Come on in when you're done. We're overdue for a visit."

I do serious work down on my knees getting the beds ready and planting the flowers. The wood chips add a nice professional touch.

I'm dying for Nana to see the finished work, but our routine calls for us to visit first. For me the conversation is the main event, anyway.

Spend time with her and you get a good idea where Dad gets his gift for gab, expressing wide-ranging and original thought and strong opinions. As much as it hurts to see how she struggles, pain and debility do not come up in our kitchen table talk. She doesn't dwell on the past, either. Nana is all about the here and now—current happenings in the world, events in my life, and my thoughts and opinions.

Today we get a critique of the media. Nana is in full huff about disrespect for the current president.

"It was on the noon news, and I couldn't believe it. This woman referred to him as 'Carter.' Imagine! Not even Mr. Carter. Shouldn't it be President Carter?"

"Of course."

"Exactly. He's the president of our country! No matter if I voted for him or not, he deserves to be spoken of correctly. I still have problems calling him Jimmy."

"Isn't that his choice?"

"For heaven's sake, Steven, was it Jimmy Buchanan instead of James? Or Georgie Washington or Abie Lincoln? Jimmy does not fit the dignity of the office."

Before she gets on a tear about something else, it's time to go out and look.

She tries to beg off, I think because she's tired and sore today, but I help her up and guide her to the door.

"What have you done to my yard?"

She insists that I help her down the back steps and walk her around all the flower beds. I can't get her to go back in until she's seen it all. I can't believe how happy I am about how happy she is.

Then, back in the house, the happiness hits an abrupt, unexpected wall. Nana tells me to get her purse. She makes a painful effort to pull out money.

"No, Nana, I can't."

"Pish tosh. Why can't you? I know those new plants weren't free."

"Mom bought them at the garden store. That's between you two."

"At least a little something for the beautiful work. That's between you and me."

I can't close her hand on the money and push it away. However gentle and loving I tried to be, that would hurt her. I just shake my head.

"Well, please yourself." I have no idea what the words, or her look, mean.

Socratic Coyote

Mid-dinner, out of the blue, we get Serious Dad. He asks—more like demands—"Did she pay you?"

"You mean Nana?"

"Who else would I mean? Did she?"

"No."

"I am already aware of why, Steve. She called and said you refused to take her money."

Oh no.

"Was she mad?"

"Angry would be the word, unless my mother was bitten by a rabid coyote."

"Please Dad, was she?"

"Is my mother upset because my son and her grandson—a favorite, too, at least 'til now—turned down her money? Is she angry or hurt? Is that what you're asking?"

Oh no, oh no, oh no. He said "hurt." This is awful! And it puts me in a worse hurt because Dad will show no mercy to anything that hurts his mother.

Like the rabid coyote he just spoke of.

"Oh, Arthur," Mom says and turns to me. "I don't believe your father's entirely serious."

"No, I'm not. But I am entirely curious. I want to understand what goes on in my son's mind, especially as it pertains to my beloved mother."

"I don't know, Dad. I just did not feel right about taking money. I couldn't."

"You say you're going to do yard work for the Utleys and the Petersons. Are you going to refuse their money, too?"

"Of course not. That's work."

"Which would seem to be exactly the same as the mowing and weeding and what-all you do for your Grandmother Anderson."

You know, he's right. No time to ponder, though, because he lets rabid Socrates out of the cage. Did I refuse the money because I think she can't afford to pay? Did it occur to me that this might be an insult? Make her feel less-than? Am I so loaded with paper route money Nana's isn't worth taking? Will I take the money next time if she offers?

Five answers in the negative, and a couple more follow. And I know, from my years of Dad-watching, that he actually likes hearing "no."

"I think we're talking about the heart, not the head."

Not All Business

"You needn't concern yourself with your grandmother's feelings, by the way."

Whew.

"'The boy does us all proud.' Those are her exact words."

He looks off into the Dad Zone like he's reading off invisible notes.

"'He's *all business*.' You've heard that, right?"

"Sure."

"Is that a good thing?"

"I guess, if somebody's in business."

"What was wrong about taking the money?"

"It felt wrong. Money has nothing to do with me helping Nana, Dad."

"An exchange of funds for services would…

"Would be like a job. Like business."

"Aha! And you, my son, are not all business. Mother's right, about doing us all proud."

"I don't understand."

"Oh, but you do. And you proved it. There are people you serve because you love them. And, serving them, you love them even more. How much money is that worth?"

"None. Or maybe a lot?"

"You are on the money! Zero dollar value, worth more millions than anyone can count. Do you think those words I dreamed up for the bank are all about business?"

"Where People Mean Everything? I do—or at least I did."

Dad chuckles, "If the slogan didn't bring in customers and money, they'd drop me and our agency like hot rocks. But here's the rest of the story, the real deal, the bigger message. This is another one you really do want to keep."

The man knows how to work a dramatic pause. Even Mom and the Sisters are dying to know what's next.

"Where People Mean Everything is a way of life, a philosophy of life. Life itself, because it makes life worth living. Never forget, there's good and then there's good."

And there's my big Huh? of the Day.

"In business, if you're any good at it, you spread good all around, do good things for people. And it's good to be fairly compensated or you can't keep doing good. Then there's the good you do just because it is...

"Good?"

"A magic word. Like dessert! Tonight, we enjoy it in honor of Nana. And after clean-up, we'll all take some to her."

Get Pedaling

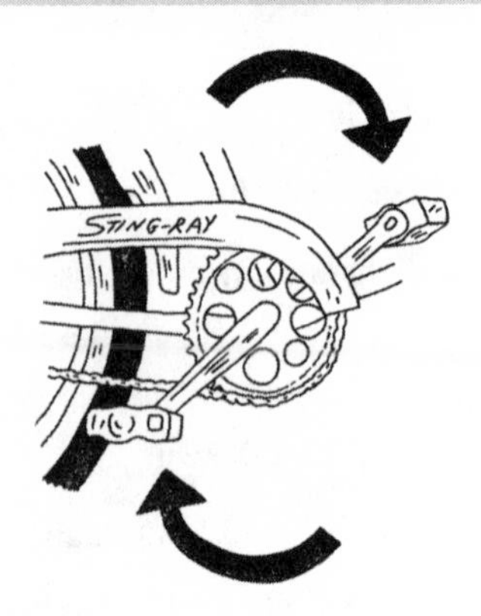

The Challenge

Understand the good you already do, in order to do more good for more people. Why? Because it's good.

Doing Good Is Not Giving Back

The extremely wise—and readable—rabbi and author Daniel Lapin hit the nail on the head about the notion of "giving back" in charity. He asks, basically, if you're giving back to society, what is it you took that you need to repay?

Doing good is giving, period. Not repayment, or prepayment, or any kind of quid quo pro. It's not transactional in any way, shape, or form.

~~giving back~~

doing good

Exercise #1: Good Work

Think about and list the good done in the course of your business.

In health care, say, you and members of your team add to people's productive life and well-being. In a happy, well-run practice, just being cared for is a positive experience. With serious conditions, you bring comfort and allay fears for patients and their loved ones.

So far, so obvious, right? But that's only the beginning. Your business, whatever it is, provides jobs with attendant financial and personal benefits for people on the team. The people you serve benefit from what you do, which has positive value for them. Why else would they choose and pay for it? On the local level, your business taxes support schools and the good things they do for kids and the community. Transacting business stimulates the economy. Good spreads like ripples in a pond and adds to people's lives.

You do more good for others in the course of business than you thought.

#2 Intentional Good

Now list your charitable giving and activities, in private, through your business, and in member groups like churches and clubs. What form does it take? Donations in money or in kind, volunteer hours, fundraising, random acts of generosity to needy people you encounter?

#3 Personal Good

What loved ones and personally connected individuals do you support and assist like I helped my Grandmother Anderson?

#4 Why You Do It

Explain what doing good does for you and the intended beneficiaries. Why does it matter for you? How does it impact them? Does it tie into your business, and, if so, what's the related purpose? And what are your purely personal rewards?

Purpose and Strategy

Define a purpose of the good you want to do. Make strategic choices to get the most good-for-buck or good-for-volunteer-hour to make the world a better place.

Make It a Fit

Do things that matter, in areas that matter to you. And in ways that suit you.

Giving that ties into your business has to relate to what you and your team do and show you in a positive light.

Get Out in Front

Remember to let your purposes and beliefs define your choices.

Don't do it just because others ask. Don't just throw money.

Mean what you're doing. Understand it and believe in it.

Your Giving Place

You'll know when you reach it.

It's Where People Mean Everything, your own way!

So...

What's your strategy for doing good and making the world a better place?

Special Events Center
VIEW FROM THE TOP

Chapter 10

Learning Opportunity

Not-Hot Ticket

Ten hours after bounding out of the house, Dad bounds back in. Just-in-time arrival for dinner means we get him in full office-boss regalia. The clothes look almost as fresh as he does. He has a smile for one and all and puts a pamphlet in front of Mom. She looks it over.

"Who printed it?"

"Presto or Provo, I don't know. Why?"

"The registration is a little off."

"Yes, and our agency's copy and design are inspired, brilliant! I'm sure the offspring agree."

Brilliant? I don't know. I do kind of wonder what comes after the big, bold lettering on the cover…

But first we pray and eat, which Dad declares an urgent necessity because we have meatloaf.

Later he says this about the pamphlet: "It's for an all-day event at the university arena. I admit that I was skeptical at first. Who wants to sit on a hard seat for eight hours while guys stand and talk? Guess what? A lot of people do. Every year the crowds get bigger!"

With a magician's flourish, he produces an envelope and says, "Hottest tickets in town in here. Any takers?"

"Truly sorry, Dad; I am otherwise engaged."

Margaret is as truly sorry as Heidi.

"You're sure? I have extras. Take your beaus and make it a double date." He's teasing. Dad knows that both girls have full-time summer jobs.

"No point in me going," Mom says. "I'm already married to a master of oratory and wisdom."

"You've got a ticket, Steve, if you want."

"Thanks, Dad. Can I borrow the pamphlet?"

"Keep it. Let me know about the ticket by tomorrow morning."

Let Sleeping Pamphlets Lie

The thing is an absolute, drop-dead no go for me. Dad, obviously, won't care. So why don't I just decline, on the spot, like the other three?

And why don't I keep quiet about the pamphlet?

Well, unlike the sisters, my "no thanks," to be spoken after dinner, will be all about summertime kid fun. I'm talking 100 percent goofing-around with friends; the day in question will be our official kickoff of summer.

The day after tomorrow, same day as the speakers' event, I will spend in pre-teen heaven. My friend Scott has invited me, Mark, Jason, and a couple other guys to be his family's guests at the Salt Lake Tennis and Swim Club!

You should see the Olympic-size pool, the crazy-high boards and platforms for diving, the cool kids and snootzy cute girls working on tans, the snack bar with hamburgers cooked to order and hand-made treats like from an ice cream parlor. If you're a member kid, like Scott, you just charge stuff to the family account. And Scott's mom says we can have what we want.

Welcome to the Club, right?

But, oh no, look at this in Dad's pamphlet…

The name of the all-day conference does more than knock off the title of a book that has a place of honor on a shelf in our family library—*See You at the Top*, the number-one bestseller about succeeding in business and life by the salesmen's super-salesman, Zig Ziglar. Dad once gave me an audio tape of a talk by Zig, who personally signed Dad's book with special thanks for all the great help and support.

Zig will speak in person at the arena. Here on Planet Anderson, this is an A-List celebrity appearance.

But no bigger than, in the flesh, the beloved TV star and humorist Art Linkletter.

And, live and in-person, Paul Harvey, news commentator on coast-to-coast radio. Him saying "Hello America . . . Stand by for the news!" has the power to stop Middle Americans in their tracks to listen. That includes Mom. Me too, for that matter.

The program lists other big deals, but these three are all it takes to throw me into turmoil and terrible conflict. I also love that the arena show is for those committed to self-improvement and reaching new heights in business success.

Impossible choice:

Recognized stars of our world, in person,
for my kind of people!

\- or -

A day in delicious summertime paradise!

Only Bike On The Rack

The arena edges out bliss. Yes, I'm surprised by this, too.

I put on school clothes, neat but not picture-day, jeans and a collared shirt a sister shows me how to iron. I stick with the usual sneakers and carry a spiral notebook, sharp pencils, food and Mom-legal noncarbonated beverages in a canvas newspaper bag.

Paradise whispers, one last time, in the voice of the cutest girl at Scott's club, "Steve, are you sure about this? You can still change your mind." But then I'm on my business bike, rollin' toward my first major-name grownup business conference. The thrill increases when I pedal past cars backed up to park for the University of Utah's 15,000-seat special events center, home of the Utes and no end of major happenings.

I lock my bike all by itself in the biggest bike rack I've ever seen. Even during the school year, when it would be packed with college students' bikes, mine would be the only purple Sting-Ray. And even at age eighteen, not twelve, I'd be the youngest person in the huge crowd of my fellow event-goers.

Here we go, streaming up the steps to the entrance, buzzing with big-deal-ness. One guy wants to buy a newspaper from me. Understandable, I guess, but also annoying. I don't ask to buy something from his briefcase, do I?

Other than that, I seem to be invisible. Maybe a seventh grader with a newspaper bag is so out of place it's easier not to see me. But guess what, I don't care. I see myself clearly. I see exactly who I am and why I belong exactly here, today, among my own kind even if I'm the only one who knows it.

Whatever you're doing, you people in business clothes, handing each other business cards, locking eyeballs and telling each other what business you're doing well in and blah-blah-blah, I will do it better.

The house is packed to the top rows with people pulled in and thrilled by the celebrity speakers they're about to behold. Just like twelve-year-old me, getting curious looks from the suits on either side of me. That stops when the speaking begins, because great speaking is great entertainment and everybody's caught up. Those who really pay attention and engage get a strong dose of inspiration and a one-day education in how to do better at whatever it is we do, while feeling better about doing better.

The youngest person in this SLC crowd may be the most engaged. Nobody takes more notes, that's for sure. If somebody's talking, I put words on paper. During the between-speech breaks, I walk around and study my business tribe. Taking it all in, sucking the special events center dry. And I love it, love it, love it.

Then I burn back home on my Sting-Ray to hit spectacular heights as the world's most successful paperboy.

Today the Foothill Neighborhood of Salt Lake City, tomorrow the World!

Socratic Me

"Delicious as ever, my dear. Now, after we clear and before the ice cream, we will have a little surprise."

"What now?" looks on faces, lightly sprinkled with "oh no."

And "uh-oh" when Dad turns my way.

"One of the great rewards of parenthood is when the kids do things you absolutely do not expect. You did that today, Steve. It was even more surprising because of what you chose to give up. At your age, I might have chosen differently."

Wait—what—he thinks I should have gone to the swim club?

"Well, was it worth it?"

"Oh my gosh!"

"Did you learn anything?"

"I filled a whole notebook with stuff they said that I need to remember!"

"Sounds like school, not summer."

"Way more interesting than school. This is stuff I want to use, like now! And anyway, I've got lots more summer."

"Bring the notebook."

"Now?"

When I bring it back and sit, Dad suggests I stand.

"You have the table, Steve, and our attention. Tell us some of the high points and best takeaways. Give us a few of your own greatest hits."

This feels weird, okay, until the excitement of the day kicks in.

I start with Zig Ziglar, how amazing he is in person. He's like the kindest, warmest guy in the world, talking to you and nobody else. He puts on a whole show just standing onstage in his suit.

"What's in the notebook from Zig?"

"Well, Mr. Ziglar said that if you want to learn and grow, that's your responsibility. You don't wait for anybody to give you what you need. You go out and get it. That might mean giving up other stuff."

"Hmmm. A bit like you and the Swim Club . . ."

Mom says, "Tell us about Art Linkletter. He's so cute and funny when he does his show with little children."

"'Get Mean in the Morning,' he said."

Mom looks a little shocked.

"He talked about 'Kids Say The Darndest Things,' too, and was very funny, Mom. But the 'Get Mean' thing seemed like his main point. It's about doing things you absolutely don't want to do. Even if you really want to put them off, you do them first thing. Mean in the Morning makes the rest of the day better!"

"Thank you, Mr. Linkletter," says Heidi. "I will be mean in the early evening and tell Doug I'm going to the lake with Todd, not him."

Margaret wants to know, "Does Paul Harvey speak in that weird radio voice in person?"

Wow, I have the attention of both sisters.

"Pretty much the radio voice," I say. "Paul Harvey's speech was called 'The Rest of the Story,' like his afternoon show. He says we should all do like him, ask people questions to get their behind-the-scenes stories. That's how you understand people and know what to do."

"How in the world could that do anybody any good?"

"Very funny, Dad. How are people everything if you don't understand their situations? I use this stuff all the time!"

"On a paper route?"

"How else do I know who needs what, to serve them? Like, Mr. Hutchinson can get up out of the wheelchair now, but he still needs his paper in the mail slot. And Mrs. Simpson takes extra time, because she's lonely. And I know you're kidding, Dad."

"That I am. Great stuff, young man, and well presented."

"There's one more."

"We are all ears."

"There was this really cool guy, Dennis Waitley, who studies winning athletes and how we can all be winners. He talked about this thing Russian athletes do, which helps them beat us in the Olympics. Before their events, they visualize themselves winning, then do it. He says everybody should do the same thing, for right now and years in the future. And he had the whole stadium be quiet and do it."

"Brilliant! Thirty seconds of visualizing the future starts now."

After the silence, Margaret speaks first: "I visualize two months from now, in college. I have my pick of sororities after rush week. And finish first semester on the high honor roll."

Heidi: "And you and I don't have to share a car."

Dad says, "The future I visualize is imminent. I am about to have butter pecan ice cream with my family."

Note from the present day: Upstairs, in a footlocker, I have the spiral-bound notebook I filled in that arena in 1978. I don't have to look at the notes to tell you what jumped out and stuck with me then. It still does, to this day.

Get Pedaling

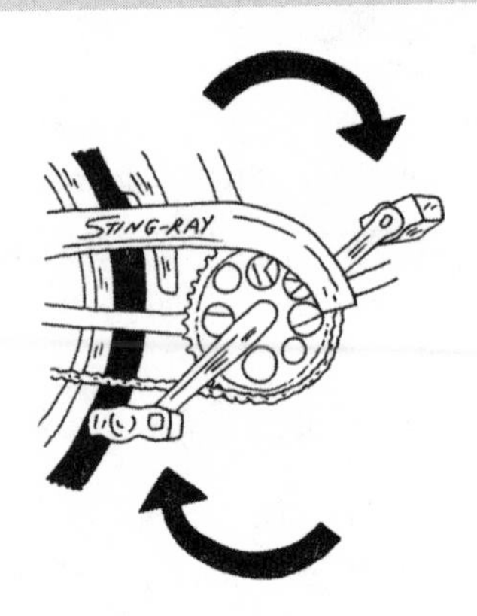

The Challenge

Seek and learn.

Take full responsibility for your own ongoing education. Know what you need to know to do better in business and in life. Figure out where and how you can learn it. Then do just that. Learn and develop yourself. Daily. Continuously.

Who's Responsible

This is all on you. The schooling you acquire for yourself is done on your initiative. It's entirely of your own design, for your own purposes.

On Whose Time

Yours.

Yes, you'll give up some goofing off, as I did when I went to the daylong famous speaker's event in SLC. But you'll be really glad, just like me at age twelve.

On Whose Dime

Yours again.

But compared to low-yield and no-yield diversions, the trade-off is a no-brainer. You are more than paid back in opportunities to do more in your work and earn more. You reap rewards that count for much more than money, too.

Consider yourself very fortunate if your organization provides its own training and development and/or helps cover the costs of off-hours education.

If not, consider yourself very fortunate anyway—you have the smarts to support your own development to do more, do it better, and feel better about it.

School Everywhere

If you pursue off-hours formal training, certification, degrees, your program may be straight-up traditional school.

Or it might be an extremely un-school-like, free-form hybrid curriculum to gain your own targeted knowledge base, skillsets, inspiration, motivation that you require for your development.

Faculty of Millions

When the student is ready, the teacher appears.

Be ready—your teachers will appear all over. Any number of people know something important for you to learn.

They could be world-famous authorities, like those who spoke at the all-day learning opportunity in this chapter, which I went to more or less by accident. Or they might be experts and geniuses whose podcasts you listen to and whose books you read. Your great teachers may have been dead for centuries or millennia.

Or they might be right at hand. Could be Charlie, who's so much more skillful at working with difficult and demanding clients than you are. Or Kathryn, who's famously brilliant at using the new systems your team just on-boarded.

Could be a full-on "A" mentor long known and of lifetime importance.

Seek, find, ask—they're there for you and eager to teach.

No Easy A

Be real, and don't flatter yourself about your newly acquired expertise and knowledge. Final grades are given out by the real, working world. Instead of Pass/Fail, it's Succeed/Fail. And it's brutal.

Time to Learn

Make time by using minutes and hours you've already got, just waiting to be used more wisely.

Learn while driving or commuting by listening to audiobooks and podcasts. Ditto gym workouts, runs, walks, getting ready in the morning.

Just for fun, count learning time as college-class equivalent. A one-hour daily commute equals five credit hours a week. Add two to three hours of exercise time, and you get the equivalent of class hours to earn a four-year college degree in ten years or less!

Recommended Reading

My previous book, *Nearly Everything I Learned in Kindergarten Screwed Me Up!* is all about growth, personal and professional, after you wind up formal schooling and begin your life's work. That is, of course, when your real, on-your-own lifetime education begins. The book lays out a program to create an inner institution of learning.

I call it Me U.

Hope and More Hope

Be motivated by hope. Be rewarded with hope.

You hope for a better future and educate yourself in hopes of achieving it. Educating yourself begets more hope, even before you make tangible gains from it—as you almost surely will. From the get-go, you learn about exciting new possibilities in life. You learn by example, by osmosis, just by tapping into the legacy of those who went before. Then hope delivers, when you use it to your own advantage.

We live on hope. It gets us out of bed in the morning. And self-education gives us more of it.

So…

What's your personal education plan?

I DARE YOU!

I DARE YOU!

DANFORTH

Chapter 11

I Dare You

Summertime Blahs

No, I can't exactly say I miss the old Dragon Lady. But boy, did she make a memorable first impression. Nobody, before or since, comes close—snarling at me, trash-talking the newspaper, making ridiculous demands while emitting smoke like she might shoot flames out of her mouth and fry me on the spot. An adventure in customer relations I cannot forget.

Where Mean People Mean Everything.

Then she got off the evening shift that she said was killing her. She also stopped smoking, which really would kill her, joined a health club, and became a new person.

Today she smiles and says, "Just a sec, Steve," writes out a check and says, "Next time I'll have it ready so you don't have to wait."

Nice. Except I get nothing fun to talk about at dinner or make my friends laugh.

Next comes a guy who says "Hi, Steve" and shouts to his wife to get the money. Then more hellos followed by waits while people get payment. Some don't even speak, just smile and gesture. Six months into my paperboy-ing, they know who I am, why I'm here, and automatically do what's expected so I can keep throwing papers on their porches. And pay me again four weeks out for more papers on porches.

Walk-around collections all dialed in. Words no longer necessary.

Today I don't even get my guaranteed no-fail talkers. Mrs. Simpson went east to visit her family. This means hours of future conversations and loads of pictures of adorable, smart grandkids when she gets back. Nada today, though. Same goes for Legendary Lowell, also on vacation. Forget about laughs. A lot of other people are away, too. But with delivery duly suspended, so it all works out with Mrs. Hanson.

Things are just so smooth, easy, pleasant on a summer's day that's breezy and perfectly not-hot, with a feeling in the air that summer's almost over. And you know what? I don't mind that it is almost over, and I'm almost back in school.

Truth #1: I'm pretty bored with summer vacation.

My friends, too—except nobody wants to say so because it goes against kidhood.

Truth #2: I'm pretty bored with the paper route, too.

This one I don't even like thinking because it goes against myself. How could I be bored today with something that was so challenging and exciting six months ago—that I absolutely loved?

Unexpected Gift

Really, how could I?

I'm about to get more time than I want to think about this on a customer's front porch.

Until now, Walter B. Tibbetts, PhD, has been a name without a face because his checks came in by mail. Now I have to stop by to collect. Probably he just forgot.

I ring and a man comes to the door, white-haired but not old-old, I'd say between Dad's age and Nana's. "Ah," he says, "I erred about your time of arrival. My apologies. You'll have to wait while I locate what I put aside for you. But it will be worth waiting for. Make yourself comfortable."

Comfortable, on a porch with no furniture? Odd, too, what he says. What's there to go get when the paperboy shows up for money except, you know, money?

He turns abruptly and says, "Where are my manners? Was I raised by stoats and weasels? I know your name, Steven J. Anderson, but you don't know mine. I am Walter B. Tibbetts, Professor Emeritus. Not to stand on formality, you may call me Prof T."

"Glad to meet you, and please, call me Steve."

“A delight to make your acquaintance, Steve,” he says and opens the door to shake hands.

A character, without a doubt. Nobody talks like this except in old movies. I may get a story for dinner after all.

While the wait stretches, I stop wondering what he’s a professor of and go back to the blahs about delivering papers. Face it—this isn’t all that difficult. After I cut the whole thing down to under an hour, get collections handled, the Mrs. Hanson stuff wired, then what?

Boredom stretches ahead because I still have a couple more years before teenager part-time jobs.

And boredom is boring to think about. Then it gets irritating.

Where is that oddball, anyway? Did he forget I’m here? Far be it for a son of Arthur S. Anderson to walk off on a customer, so I keep waiting.

Finally he comes back and gives me the payment envelope. “Already prepared for you. Easy peasy lemon squeezy. That’s from a British detergent ad, don’t you know.”

If it was ready, Prof, what took you?

He holds the answer: a book with a red leather cover. “Written in 1931, here in a 1958 special edition. I purchased a whole case, and I had to hunt for the last one remaining. Both old and brand spanking new. No one has ever opened it. You have never read it. Now you must!”

He looks deep into my eyes, hands me the book, and says, "I Dare You!"

That seems like a little much until I see *I Dare You!* is the title, stamped into the fancy leather cover. The book looks and feels important. The Prof places his hands over mine on the book, like I'm taking an oath.

"I dare you," he says, this time more like he's daring me.

"I just gave you a check, as I do every month. Your percentage is well and truly earned. You do a fine job, young man."

“Thank you, Prof.”

“A fine job, indeed. What is far more important is that you grow into a fine young man. Finer than any job you ever do.”

He points to my heart and head, saying, “Finer here . . . and here.”

“That is the essence of William H. Danforth’s dare. He, the author, once dared me in person. Unforgettable. Even if I presented you with a great fortune, this book has far greater value.”

“I’ll start reading right away.”

“That you will, without a doubt. Now you to your tasks and me to mine. On page 67, Mr. Danforth dares us old geezers to *plan a daring program to crown the years of our life*. And I take the dare!”

Vacation Reading

Could the man talk or what? Wow. That was Dad-grade but from a hundred years back.

I start reading right after collection. Partly because I said I would. And Prof T was like a secret neighborhood wizard. Oz on Emerson Avenue. And, you know, there’s not much else to do.

Also—the Prof has no way of knowing this—at age twelve I already have a proven interest in classic self-help/business literature. Back in the third grade, Mrs. Stirk gave us an assignment to pick a book, with her approval, and read it. I made my selection with great care from the family library: the all-time classic, *How to Win Friends and Influence People* by Dale Carnegie, first published in 1936.

That makes it five years newer than the book from the Prof, which I see in the opening few pages was by a guy who seriously walked the talk. The author came out of nowhere to found a huge food company, Ralston-Purina. "I dare you" is like a battle cry, a slogan to work and live by. A lot like our own Where People Mean Everything.

Honestly, I have to make myself read the first dozen or so pages. Blame the blahs, not the words. Then, right about when I feel like doing something else, there's this:

Make something happen! Break a window, if necessary!

Now it's like this business giant who passed away twenty-three years earlier talks to me and nobody else. Who broke a window a few months back? I didn't mean to do it, but you better believe it made something happen. I went from horrible shame, with glass all over the nice lady's porch, to a new level of customer service with a whole new level of customer. Not just satisfied, but loyal!

It is on, man, with me and the book.

The voice that speaks is forceful and exciting. Over and over, like a drumbeat, it dares me to get up and do something big. To stand taller, get stronger and healthier, have big ideas and follow through on them, develop my spiritual side, do more with other people, and for them. Each dare is like a twofer—the guy with a big voice dares me to share the benefits with others. Dare, dare, dare; share, share, share. Right here and right now. The book—I should say this person in the book who gets in my face—is relentless.

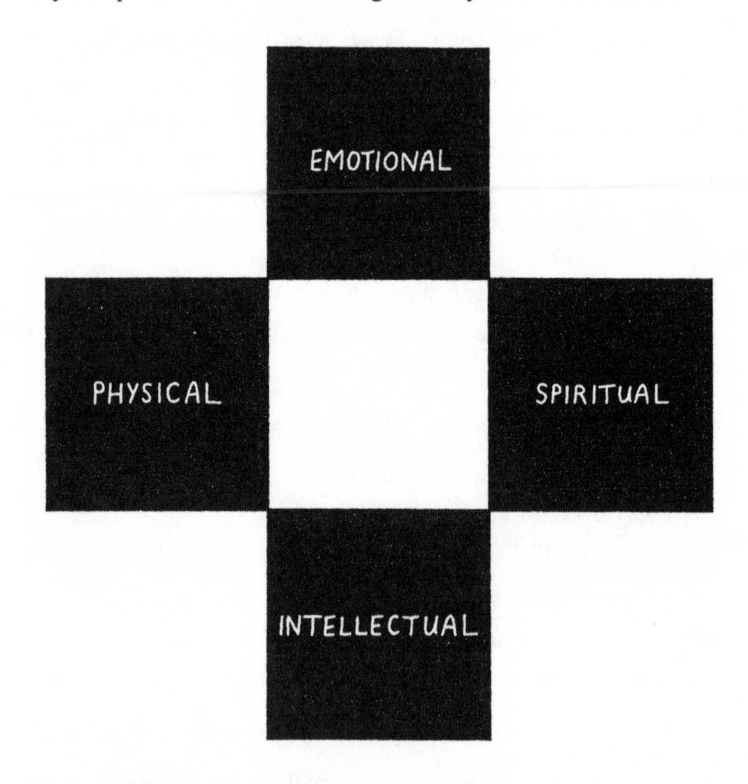

Behind it all is a system, which he tells me to draw out on paper. I make four squares, like part of a checkerboard. I label them: Mental. Spiritual. Physical. Social. I have to work on each area constantly. I must build them equally, and the building never stops.

I read 'til the very last second to start my route. When my route bags are fully packed, I put the book in with the papers so it rides with me.

So much for the blahs.

Daring Dessert

"I dare you to tell me where you got that! And what you make of it."

I knew Dad would have something to say about the book. This is why I carried it into dinner and put it on the table.

When I tell him how I got it, he says, "Hmm. Interesting. When the student is ready, the teacher appears . . ."

"You know about the book, Dad?"

"Are you kidding me? Of course. Much as I admire Socrates, Danforth doubled down on the ancient Greeks. 'Sound of mind and sound of body,' they said. He added spiritual life and social connection. He wrote that book as training material for his employees, you know."

"He says so, yes. But I'm not sure why."

"It's not obvious to you?"

"No. It's for people in his business, but it's not exactly about business."

"Exactly! The Danforth Dare is about building better people to do better business. He focused on human development, Steve. Who we are comes first. What we do follows."

"But what we do brings in money and builds business."

"I am so happy you're bringing this up! It's the rest of the story, about Where People Mean Everything."

"How?"

"Great people do great customer service. Be the right person and doing right comes more naturally and a lot more easily."

"My business is me?"

"Being, not doing, Steve. This is the final challenge. The job behind the job, whatever line of work you choose. Even if it's work you don't choose but take out of necessity. Even if it gets repetitive and, what's the word . . ."

"Boring?"

Dad chuckles. "Even the best work in the world feels that way from time to time when things get a little too routine. Lack of challenge is stultifying, Steve, stupefying. But you will never lack for challenge if you build yourself, every day, in vital areas."

"Like the squares?"

"Yes."

"But, Dad?

"Yes?"

"Then the work never ends, does it?"

"Do you want it to?"

"No, I guess not."

"You know you don't, Steve. And I know that it's time for dessert. You and I will do the work of slicing and serving."

Out in the kitchen, we carefully cut portions from a big pan of Mom's lemon squares, one of her all-time hits. Then he and I cut each square into four and separate them to make a mini-checkerboard.

We carry the plates out and Dad proclaims, "Self-improvement, à la Anderson. Danforth squares that taste like heaven!"

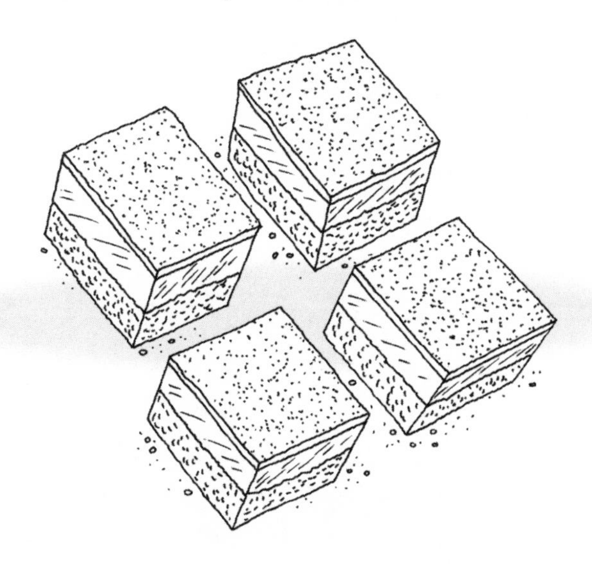

Get Pedaling

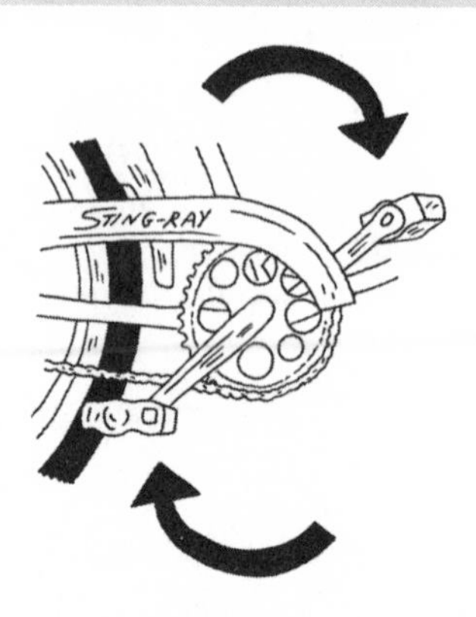

The Challenge

The author William H. Danforth lays this one out in his book, *I Dare You!*

"You have a four-fold life to live: a body, a brain, a heart and a soul—these are your living tools. To use and develop them is not a task. It is a golden opportunity."

Look within and seize the opportunity. Be better!

Danforth dared us all way back when. I dare you now.

Take the dare.

Redefine Service

This time Where People Mean Everything is all about you. You mean everything. And your Being gets out ahead of Doing.

Make a new Service Promise to and for yourself. Focus on

what you can do to continually improve and be better in each of the four vital areas that Danforth depicted as squares…

Mental – What are you doing to grow in knowledge, skill, intellect, and wisdom?

Social – What are you doing to expand and deepen your social connections and your abilities to effectively deal with people?

Spiritual – What are you doing to connect to the beliefs and values that you hold dearest?

Physical – What are doing to improve in health, strength, endurance, and overall wellness?

Define a vision for improvement, and ultimate goals, in each of your squares.

Maintain Balance

Keep moving in all four areas to stay balanced and upright.

Riding my Sting-Ray with pounds and pounds of newspapers was a balancing act. Balance came much more easily when I was in motion. Still, I had to continually make adjustments to stay upright.

So it goes with life.

Get moving. Make something happen. Break a window if you have to, and make adjustments as you go.

I dare you!

So…

What's your four-square personal development plan?

Where
People
Mean
Everything
2242

Chapter 12

Where People Mean Everything

Ranger Wendy's Perfect Storm

Morning in the High Uinta Mountains: A few of us light sleepers get to enjoy a little peace before the whole scout troop wakes up. I lie in the tent and listen to birds and a stream tumbling into the alpine lake we're camped near. Here, above treeline in mid-September, snow will start piling up soon. But this trip we get some leftover summer.

I hear Mr. Bill talking with somebody. Then, more serious and louder than usual, he addresses the whole troop.

"Listen up, guys. I want you wide awake right now. You will give your complete attention to my new friend Wendy, the district backcountry ranger."

"Good morning, scouts! I've got more campers to locate, so this'll be quick. It is time to get out of the high country. There is a rapidly growing threat of thunderstorm activity in this area. Individuals have been killed by lightning strikes right where we are now. I know, because I led the body recovery team. Watch your footing on the down-mountain hike."

"What do we say to Ranger Wendy, gentlemen?"

Still in our bags, we yell "Thank You!" at a person we don't actually see.

Then we shoot like human cannonballs out of official BSA backpacking tents. Even my famously hard to wake up tent buddy Chris, aka Sleeping Beauty, is up and at 'em. The sky's still clear, but you can count on guys later telling highly exaggerated tales of almost getting zapped. And, of course, the she-ranger and dead bodies.

I have to say that packing fast—like our lives depend on it—and beating feet down the trail is kinda fun. Nobody moans about heavy packs or groans about skipping the hot campfire breakfast, always a high point. And I have my own private reason not to mind. If we get to the cars earlier than usual, as we surely will, I'll have more time at home before the drop-off of newspapers for my route. The tight turnaround every fourth Saturday has always been a back-of-mind concern. And I, as you've probably noticed, am a concerned kind of kid.

We're low on a timbered slope, less than a mile from the cars, when boiling clouds gather overhead. There's rumbling in the distance up high and behind us. But not a drop of rain falls on us. Sun breaks through when we get to the parking lot at the trailhead. Hungry scouts share a delicious thought: There's a fire pit and picnic area. Why not stop and cook breakfast?

Why not is that the storms are barely getting started, and now the whole area is under major flash flood warnings. One side road is already washed out.

This we know because District Ranger Wendy personally tells us. How on earth did she get down here first? And, you know, wow. She's like this superhero Viking queen in a freshly pressed U.S. Forest Service uniform that she somehow had time to change into. Heck with breakfast—the entire troop has a crush.

Ranger Wendy becomes an instant legend on a day that will also be legendary for the troop's all-time longest trip back to Salt Lake because of (a) debris on the road from runoff, (b) a long one-lane-at-a-time road construction area, (c) backups ten times worse than usual because everybody and his brother gives up on fun in the mountains and flees, and (d) everything slowed down by the on-and-off rain.

Sitting in Mr. Bill's Jeep, alternately creeping and stopping, I realize I don't have a prayer of getting back to make on-time six o'clock delivery. This I figure out miles and hours from home. But having figured it out, there's no way to deal with it. Pre-cellphone, I have no way to call and make arrangements. There's nothing to do but silently freak out.

I picture my customers waiting, looking, wondering where their papers are on the day they want them most. When you're home all day on Saturday, the paper is something to look forward to. People use it to plan their evenings—check restaurant ads, movie listings, and showtimes. Our phone will be ringing off the hook. Mom won't know what to say. Dad, too, will get involved. Big "Oh no" about that. Here's another: With an epic whole-route fail like this, Mrs. Hanson will get in on the act, too.

I try for a comforting thought. Maybe, just maybe, I have built up enough goodwill that customers will forgive and forget. And I can dream up some kind of mass Great Recovery, like after the paper-through-window incident. Of course, this is seventy houses instead of one, and a lot of the folks aren't as nice as Smashed Window Lady.

The perfect storm roars in my head. "Oh no!" booms instead of thunder. Our lateness seems worse because Salt Lake City's dry when we finally get there. I'm poised to leap out, speed-fold papers, and break world paperboy records. I'll do Whatever It Takes to make things right with customers.

Ready to jump and run.

Not ready to see my purple bike coming down the street as Mr. Bill's Jeep goes up. I am so not ready to see who's on the bike that I look twice and make a conscious effort to process the visual input.

Dad rides the Sting-Ray, newspaper bags swinging on the ape-hanger bars.

Small Bike, Big Deal

The Schwinn neither fits nor flatters my father. A bike with twenty-inch wheels cannot comfortably accommodate a tallish man. Wrong-ness registers high on the Richter scale at the clash between a metallic purple bike tricked out as a kid hot rod and Dad's entire being. Even in Saturday casuals he is unmistakably a dignified man of substance. And he's anything but anonymous. Arthur S. Anderson is widely known and instantly recognizable as a leader in business, charity, and his church. Nobody doesn't know who this is, especially here in his home neighborhood.

In front of this world that knows him well, he manages to tame the Sting-Ray and put it to work.

In a wobbly sort of way.

And wow, is he a terrible shot. I see him miss a porch by a mile, dismount, and pull the paper out of some bushes.

Some kids I know would want to crawl under the car seat and die lest somebody else see their father like this.

But as what I see sinks in, I say to myself, "This is so cool!"

Cooler and cooler, to this day. And plenty cool back then. I get home flush with emotion that goes beyond gratitude. Dad does me more than a mere favor, a favor he never would do if I could figure it out and deal with it on my own.

I feel some surprise because I am not accustomed to parental bailouts. Recognition of what happened and what it means keeps getting bigger. This is a revelation, nothing less, about Dad…

And what I mean to him.

While he's still out on the route, I reconstruct the event: Dad loves to spend whole Saturdays fixing and maintaining stuff around the house. He does it the way he does all things, with purpose and focus, as if even little things are big. But all the while, wide-beam fatherly radar operates. Dad notices I'm not back when my papers get dropped off and that I'm still not home later. He knows I have no control over my lateness.

As a parent now on his fourth paperboy, he knows exactly what has to happen to get papers on porches by six o'clock. And he pivots from house D.I.Y. to fixing my paper route.

On-time delivery is good for the customers, sure. But he does not do it just for them, or for Mrs. Hanson, my reputation and standing in my work, or anybody or anything but…

Me.

For me and nobody else. This I know because I feel it.

Today I discover that I mean the world to Dad.

If you've read this far and paid any attention, this won't seem like much of a discovery. Arthur S. Anderson is the ultimate Family Man in his own private Where People Mean Everything. The "Where" is home and family. "People" are us, the Andersons. Here in my book, the light of Dad's absolute love for his family shines mostly on me. In life, it shines on us all.

Particularly while we are growing up, we miss huge things in our lives that often are obvious to others.

Then the things jump up and surprise us.

So it goes for me on Dad's Sting-Ray Saturday.

Real Life

Over the years I have come to understand Where People Mean Everything the way Dad lived it. It's much more than a way of thinking, communicating, and behaving to succeed in business. No doubt about its efficacy there—it achieves positive results, every which way, to the great benefit and happiness of you, your associates, and your clientele. But in real life, well and fully lived, the "People" and the "Everything" are not delineated by business, and the benefits go far beyond the practical.

Dad's life exemplified a way of being based on service. His slogan embraced a whole philosophy of life—and of love. It embraces the people who are truly everything to him. They're not just anybody, as associates and paying clientele can be; they are those closest, who matter most.

These are the people in whose service you ultimately work and live. You must be mindful of them always, asking yourself, "Who are these people? What can I do for them?" There's nothing servile about this kind of service—witness my father's towering stature and influence for us, his Everything People. His service to others, especially in our family, was heroic. And it was never a big deal, at least not to him.

This came clear much later when I wrote up a series of one-page stories about some of the most memorable things my parents did. One of them was Dad doing my Saturday paper route in September 1978. As I have made clear, this was a defining event, a milestone in my life. But guess what? Dad had no recollection of it. None! He didn't fail to remember so much as he didn't bother to stick a pin in it. Dad was being Dad—that's all. His not remembering, because it wasn't a big deal, makes it an even bigger deal to me.

Back then, having lived the lesson, Dad doesn't say a thing about it.

He knows that I know and I know that he knows. We communicate in a quiet, eye-to-eye, guy-to-guy moment. Dad ends it with a smile and a wink.

I don't think Socrates plans to join us for Saturday night dinner. Dad calls down the Sisters and announces that Mom and he have decided we're going out. Huge news! We practically never go to restaurants.

"We leave it to you kids to choose the dining establishment. Two stipulations: Choose quickly. I am ravenous after riding that ridiculous thing Steve calls a bike. Also, our restaurant must have a wide range of desserts with a complete selection of both fruit and cream pies, made on the premises. And lemon meringue!"

"Dad, there's only one place like that. We always go there."

"Well then, good choice. I salute your excellent judgment!"

Get Pedaling

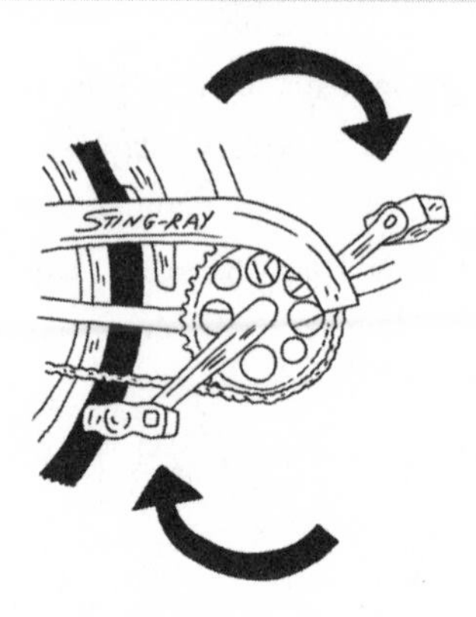

The Challenge

Know the People Who Mean Everything to you. Who are they? Give them names and faces…

- Family and loved ones
- Friends
- Team members
- Customers
- Community
- Humanity

Now that you know who they are, how will you serve them better, using all the principles of Where People Mean Everything?

So…

What is your personal *"Where People Mean Everything"* plan?

NEWS
Schwinn
STING-RAY

Forward!

Yes, it's the end of the book, where traditional usage calls for an Afterword. Not here. It's time to point forward, to riding your own route.

Bicycle to Book

It is one thing to see the purple 1965 Schwinn Sting-Ray bike in my garage and stop, smile, and pedal in memory on streets in Utah 1,200 miles away and forty-some years ago.

It is another thing entirely to get on the bike and ride it. I found this out the hard way a few years back when I decided to pedal the purple bike into a hotel ballroom where I was doing a large event. The point was to get the crowd's attention and set up the first public telling of Dad's ride on the Sting-Ray to deliver my newspapers. I expected the story and the bike ride to be one-offs. The story was not, obviously. The jury's still out on future rides.

Thank heaven I decided to practice on the Sting-Ray first. I remembered riding it to be perfectly easy and natural. Yeah, right. Elbows and knees jutted out to the sides, the pedal-spin too tight, everything wrong in shape and size for a grownup. Even after I (kind of) got the hang of it, yesteryear's supercool ride shredded grownup dignity and aplomb.

My entrance on the Sting-Ray got a bigger reaction than anticipated. I rode out to a mass gasp of surprise and laughing applause. The bike was an instant sensation. I guess we all have inner kids who still love these Schwinn Sting-Rays.

So long as we don't have to ride them.

Pleased as I was to achieve the intended public-speaking effects, I had no notion that a purple bike with twenty-inch tires could be ridden through a whole book. And that today I could deliver the essential lessons about customer service and service as a way of life the way I learned them—on my old paper route, with Dad's mentoring. It took a couple years for the thing to unpack itself, but it all began with that grown-up bike ride to the podium. And the real star revealed himself. The bike was just a stage effect to warm people up. When they all stood and cheered, some teary-eyed, at the end of the tale of Dad's Sting-Ray Saturday, they cheered for Dad. My mentor, my hero, my father still comes vividly alive on that Sting-Ray bike in 1978.

The bedrock lessons of service in business and in life that I learned on my paper route, I learned because Dad taught them and, more so, because of the way he taught. He drew lessons from the real-life experience and challenges that he insisted all his children have. He led me to learn from the paper route. He didn't push but helped me pull lessons from reality. Dinner table Socrates-ing was a guided quest to find the truth myself—and then put the truth to work.

Above all, Dad taught by example. Lessons lived by a grownup are incredibly powerful to an impressionable youngster in need of teaching and love.

To Dad, teaching was love.

Essential Elements

As I say, it took some time to unpack. Then the old, essential elements came alive. That silly bike carried me to formative real-world experience and understanding. I sat again at our big round dinner table, where Socratic Dad led me to understand and internalize lessons from reality—and, above all, to use them. We learn from experience, yes, but there must be a mentor to interpret for reality and clarify its lessons.

The bike. The paper route. The dinner table. The loving mentor. And let us not forget, Dad's words…

Where People Mean Everything

For me, they don't just unpack, they explode into Dad's philosophy of service as a way of business and of life. His Everything is a lot.

It means…

- Making and living up to a Service Promise, expressed in your own words, that defines your mission to serve your clientele. (Chapter 1, Where People Mean Everything)
- Setting and meeting a high Service Standard, so customer relations stand on solid Right, Right, Right performance. (Chapter 2, What Everything Means to People)

- Understanding and sorting out top priorities, distinguishing between tasks that are yours to do, i.e., your job, versus your tasks to be delegated and shared. (Chapter 3, When Priorities Collide)
- Being ever-mindful of the high cost to be paid when you don't live up to your words. (Chapter 4, When People Don't Mean Everything)
- Making Great Recoveries after lapses in service transforms satisfied customers into loyal customers, your gold standard clientele. (Chapter 5, More than Right)
- Creating a Feedback Culture to use customer feedback to maximum benefit and learning not to be overwhelmed by what people say they want. (Chapter 6, Everything for Everybody)
- Owning all for which you are responsible and accountable, no blaming or complaining, and staying on top of "little stuff" that's actually huge. (Chapter 7, Where the Bucks Stop)
- Doing absolutely Whatever It Takes to maintain the Service Standard and meet customer expectations. (Chapter 8, Snow Day)
- Doing good by being of service to others outside of business. (Chapter 9, Doing Good)
- Seeking out mentors who inspire and instruct in areas vital to your success. (Chapter 10, Learning Opportunity)
- Improving the whole person every day, by focusing on being—not just doing. (Chapter 11, I Dare You)

- Making your whole world Where People Mean Everything, grounded in service to those who matter most. (Chapter 12, Where People Mean Everything)

Looking back, it comes clear that Dad's words came most alive on the Saturday when he got on the Sting-Ray and delivered newspapers. That day he showed by example what Where People Mean Everything means 24/7.

Riding the bike into the ballroom, I felt a new rush of gratitude for Dad's numberless gifts and quiet fatherly heroics. And his practical lessons and deeper wisdom, some of which I have done my best to share with you.

When Dad got on the purple Sting-Ray and rode it farther than I ever will, the bike didn't fit him any better than it does me. And he didn't do it—as I did—for effect, so others could see. Indeed, he did it in spite of being seen.

He did it because it needed doing. And he lived in a world where we all can live…

Where People Mean Everything.

Enjoy the ride.

About the Author

Steven J. Anderson is an entrepreneur, author, presenter, philanthropist, and agent for creating a "Where People Mean Everything" customer service culture in organizations.

You can find him at www.StevenJAnderson.com

Where People Mean Everything® is a customer service philosophy and way of life. The Bicycle Book is a guide for creating a Where People Mean Everything culture and the systems to support it. Implemented by professionals, team members and entire organizations, the systems embodied in The Bicycle Book have the power to propel an organization to higher levels of remarkable success.

As an entrepreneur, Steve has co-created multiple organizations. Here are just a few examples:

The Crown Council - www.CrownCouncil.com – Creating a Culture of Success in Your Practice. The home for top dental practices that are committed to an ongoing, never-ending process of improving and delivering exceptional clinical care and patient service in a Culture of Success. For information call: 1-800-CROWN-58 or log onto www.CrownCouncil.info.

ToPS Institute - www.TotalPatientService.com – Team specific training, live seminars, and in-office coaching for creating a Culture of Success.

Smiles for Life Foundation - Dentistry's cause-related charity having raised nearly $50 million for children's and dental health related programs making access to care more available to those with intellectual and developmental disabilities. Discover how you can participate as a patient, practice or business. www.SmilesForLife.org.

Eagle University – www.EagleUniversity.org – Youth leadership training helping high school and college age students get a 7-year head start on their career. Week-long Eagle U courses give students the secrets, skills, and strategies to advance their careers and their lives beyond the ordinary.

As a presenter, Steve speaks at conventions and meetings around the world.

For more information on having a presentation at your next meeting, log onto www.StevenJAnderson.com or call: 1-877-399-8677

Peter Arkle's distinctive illustrations are known worldwide. They have appeared in *The New Yorker, The New York Times, Bloomberg Business Week*, covers for *TIME Magazine*, and illustrated books and major ad campaigns. www.peterarkle.com

Book Editor/Producer Mike Steere lives in Los Angeles, where he writes, edits, and consults on books, freelance journalism, and screen projects, including film adaptation of his work. His literary genius has guided the printed works of Steve Anderson for decades.

Other Books

These are just a few of the favorite things we have created that people rave about. Order online and enjoy.

Available at **www.StevenJAnderson.com**

Nearly Everything I Learned in Kindergarten Screwed Me Up!

The Culture of Success

The 13 Biggest Mistakes Parents Make and How to Avoid Them

You Can Do It

You Can Do It Better

You Can Do It Best

You Can Do It 365 Days Better

On Eagle's Wings

See Deeper

Born From Fire

Never Stand Alone